Evolution of a Soul

By Shelby Kottemann

EVOLUTION OF A SOUL

Willow Tree Press
Wisconsin, US 53572

ISBN 978-1-7379087-0-8 (paperback)
ISBN 978-1-7379087-1-5 (hardcover)

Printed in the United States of America.

What People Are Saying

"This powerful author picture-painted her heart and soul through deep, unique expressions of words and experiences. You will be left with inspirational thoughts, a positive mindset, and a desire to achieve your best."
—Toni Stone Bruce
CEO/Founder Precious Stones 4 Life LLC

"Read it slowly because the truths take time to fully develop in your soul. Then cherish it, like a fond memory that is remembered over and over."
—Elda Robinson
Retired teacher
Facebook: Bowtie Shoes

"Her unity with nature touched me deeply as I felt the connection for myself."
—Karen Wright
International Best Selling Author, *Now or Never, Shine Baby Shine*

"Beautiful, heart-felt journey of challenging life moments turned into lessons. Great read!"
—Elle Ballard
Speaker

A Note to the Reader

Welcome to Allie's Story

Allie is a young lady with a big and open heart. She connects with others and with nature, and she *feels* keenly. She sees deeper meaning in the simplicities of life.

Even though Allie was mentally and emotionally abused growing up, that's not all. Allie was also loved and nurtured. Many people came into her life that sculpted the dimensions of her heart. She found deep meaning in the simplicities of life and savored the love she found in these places.

Still, as she matured, Allie found cycles in her life that would not go away. She knew she must face her pains and look inward at the places which did not bloom if she ever were to be free to live the life she always wanted. She needed to accept and honor her truth.

By navigating the complexities of the human heart, Allie works to heal her past and her future. She finds that life blossoms from both love and pain, especially when she decides to honor herself. Can a person co-create their life with God? Are we truly able to discover ourselves when we seek our own hearts? By considering Allie's story, may you be inspired to look within your own heart and lean on faith. May you consider life and love to the depths of all they are.

Reading the chapters

As you read *Evolution of a Soul*, you will find the chapters are a bit different than most.

They're shorter.

When Allie reflected, she felt it best to do so in small doses. It helped Allie process deeply with a knowing of what God was calling forth within her heart. It felt fitting to share Allie's story in this same way. May these chapters stir your heart deeply.

I guide your reading experience with two chapter labels.

These labels are *Life* and *Reflections*.

Life: These chapters share both Allie's story and the impacts so many people made, those whom Allie believes God placed on her path. May each of these chapters shine a beaconing light for you in personal ways.

Reflections: In these chapters, you'll dive deeper to find insights Allie garnered through her bond with nature. May these chapters serve as testaments to God's guidance that unfolds within you too. If you don't believe in God, you might consider these chapters examples of faith because faith can mean different things to all of us.

There are a few illustrations.

Adults can have them too! They add meaning.

Privacy.

As with most true stories, the privacy of all who've touched Allie's life has been protected by the changing of their names.

Acknowledgements

When I think back on whom to acknowledge in the publication of my book, the list is nearly endless. The existence of this manuscript, from its inspirations to its placement into the world, is a testament to the magnitude of relationships. From small chance encounters to lifelong connections, each person who has touched my life has made a lasting impression on my heart. If you're one of those people, reading these words . . . thank you. Sincerely, from the bottom of my heart, thank you for being you, for investing a part of yourself in me, and for shining your light for me to see.

Life: Into the Woods

Tucked away in an old forest, lives a place never inhabited enough by man to be forgotten. A place where nature still stands proud in its greatest forms, bringing majestic beauty that strikes awe into the hearts of every believer and a knowing that what lies before your eyes is a masterpiece that could only be formed by the hand of our Creator. How else could something be so beautiful? Who else could place brand new colors into the sunset that never quite have a name? In this land, so much meaning speaks to the soul because God really is in the details. He tends to them.

Most people don't even realize the existence of this place on our map, but I do. I adore every square inch of it in all its magic and mystery. I welcome you into these dense piney woods, blanketed with soft copper needles that silence one step, making you feel as though you're walking sure-footedly with moccasins. I welcome you with me to know this earth like the back of your hand, the white-green lichen that crunches under the next, giving you a small, child-like, thrill through your stomach, wanting to crunch it just a little bit more. Step through the knee-high ferns and over mossy logs, unless perhaps you give in to the temptation to turn one over, in which case, you might surprise a smooth, gray salamander into scurrying for the safety of reclusion.

Before you even see it, you'll know that you're nearing water, for by time you get there, you'll be assaulted by an onslaught of the many winged and buzzing residents of this land. The ones who are only out for one thing: your blood. Consider it your fare onto this natural ride. They've probably already crawled up your socks too. You just won't realize it until tomorrow.

When you come upon the pond, stop to take it in. The glassy water. The stillness of silence as nature forgets you're there. Life in all its marvelous forms takes the show once again. The dragonflies race, the butterflies lilt, the frogs sing like they're calling, "I'm home." Fish flip their tails over the glassy surface, breaking the beautiful mirror of the skyline, but not your reverie, because in this moment you realize you and this world are one and the same. And in your quietness, in your respect for it, nature knows that you honor it and shares its gifts in return.

There is so much about love that these woods has to teach you. As you traverse its landscape, you can't help but wonder at how connected we were created to be.

Granted there are all kinds in all places, this land draws a certain kind of person to it. One whose eyes see with the soul. Ears hear with the heart. These individuals are at once greatly gifted and heavily weighted for the depth with which they perceive the world, receive the world, and give back. It's something innately earned. Only their biological, metaphysical, allegorical journey can speak to it. Their trials and triumphs are in equal measure felt immensely, immeasurably, through. They know well the worthy cost of living by the heart and soul. Different. Then again, isn't different what we were all meant to be when we're striving to remember we're the same?

Open your heart, feel your soul so you may know the gentle stirrings the elements of this land will bring. Once you are open, ne'er again will you be bored by the buds from the trees, the whirl in the breeze. When you see with the soul, you too will know. It's the little things that speak of Love, of Truth, of Faith. For God is in the details. Beautifully.

Love, it seems, comes in infinite forms. And yet, as one and the same, it is simply Love. It's what we're made of and what we strive for every day. Our journeys challenge us to seek it, to express it to reach farther beyond the trains of our story. Our journeys in this life give us one greatest challenge: a million little choices. Choose truth, faith, and love.

In a world filled with choices, the one which is best for you is where your soul will lead. What you must do is listen with ears that hear your own heart and eyes that turn inward toward your own soul. Your soul has a direct connection with God. As if deep within, you know your own plan and your purpose, if only you tap in and be true. Even on the murkiest day, that is the surest way.

Faith is most steadfast when found. Truth is most treasured when accepted. Love is purest when known it is there always. However, this tale is a story, a true one at that. And as you probably know, stories are best lived than told. That leaves me to step back and show you one path.

In this world belongs a girl who has spent many a sunny afternoon, much a misty morning, pondering such things. She can't help but do so in a land where she was meant to be. A girl born wise. A child young at heart but wise to the ways of her spirit, her land, her path. She stands on the edge of the glass-water pond, letting the breeze lift the wings of her spirit.

In the years she visited the forest with the pond, this girl already knew what love was. And she knew what it was not. For in this journey called life, she had been gifted with a home in a different world than this. A world in which she discovered the polarity of love.

This world of her youth was one full of love and hate, thoughtfulness and apathy, investment and worthlessness, security and fear, respect and spite, empowerment and undermining, encouragement and competition, pride and resentment. It was here she learned.

It seems a law of human nature that lessons are learned most fully when experienced. The trials of choice, change, and loss gave her the greatest opportunities of all. For before she understood them, it was her trials that formed a path to the dreams she had cast upon the spellbound sky.

Dreams of love, of freedom, of peace and truth, of purity and home. She dreamt from her heart, her spirit, her soul, and as with all things, she did so with all of herself, one hundred percent. It was on her path to her dreams that she saw a million glimpses of how polarities converge. But somewhere along the way, when they're cast in faith to God, dreams converge too by His hand of synchronicity.

It was on her path she grew in her journey with faith. And somewhere in the journey, as polarities and dreams converged, she stepped into a new way of being. She came to understand.

That girl is me, Allie, and it's time for me to live my journey with you.

Reflection: The Night

Take care to watch the sky in these woods, for the night can come quickly, turning the lower story into a spooky place, so black you'd never find your nose. These woods are rich in brooks and streams that darken at night so black that when you pass them by you feel as though they are holes that go right through the Earth. If perchance you did linger in the birches and poplars and spruce past the daylight hours, you would wisely find that in a clearing is a place where the sky is filled with infinite stars. From twinkling bright white to milky hues of distant light, this sky, so dimensional, sends a resonance through your spirit, the understanding of just how deep our universe spans.

Reflection: **Sky**

I remember when I first saw it.

When I was a little girl, I used to lay awake in bed with amazed, mind-boggled, wonder at the depthful starry sky; the unending universe and the idea that there could be more than just us. I wasn't sure if it scared me, impressed me, or just simply sparked my desire all the more to learn and know the world around me. But I've always been drawn to those stars.

Nowhere in the world have I seen with my very own eyes the infinite reaches of those stars and felt them in my bones as I have when I gaze into the pitch-black sky up here. Where the Milky Way's name goes without explaining. In spite of the caring, warning calls of my mother, I find myself drawn to that sky at night, unafraid of the woodsy, wild dark. Sometimes, I'd sneak out of bed just to look out the window and lose track of time gazing out at it. Lose count of the shooting stars that, in reality, don't shoot but rather swirl and glide across the void.

I sleep. I wake. Early is best. For in the wee hours, I catch a moment with quiet space, pure connections, and peace. I gaze out the window again, our lens to the universe . . .

Embers of pale yellow give rise to lime green that melt into blue from a light that draws the blend of colors up to touch a midnight black sky. And as if with the tap of one finger, the light of dawn's rising sun sends a surge of deep blue across the vast, starry sky.

As those colors touch night into day, our effervescent stars are mysteriously hidden until night allows them to light our way again. But a few of the brightest remain for hours. They shine as intently as ever before. They remind me that stars never leave us. The magic feeling they give me when I gaze up at them of a night can be found if only I remember they are there. Seen or not, they are with me, guiding in the night, holding fast in the day. Just as the sun's world holds us in reverse.

The dawn's light against the coal black silhouettes of tall pine forests move the spirit. They show a different point of view of these strong and steady creatures that have stood much longer than I. The glowing backdrop magnifies every contour of their sculpted journey, how they've been cast from the wind, toward the sun and the rain. When we pause a moment, we feel the magic, knowing they're a little like us all.

The rings of a tree are a snapshot of what it has experienced in its years of life. Plentiful years of growth and slim years of little rain when it barely survived. Those rings stay stored inside its trunk. A private memory of where it's been. The trials it's overcome, and if survived, made it stronger. That's what scientists term adaptation. But before adaptation comes persistence. Persistence in response to life's elements seems to be its greatest strength of all.

Life: **Frogs and Spaces**

When I was a little girl, I wore pretty dresses with lace-trimmed socks that my mother chose lovingly for me. I even played dress up like a Victorian lady from time to time, but more than anything, I liked being in nature. Walks in the woods, finding buckeyes, flipping over logs to look for salamanders, catching butterflies, doing most things naturey was, well, natural.

That said, it should come as no surprise that my favorite place in the whole wide world has always been these woods, wild and pure. With these vast forests and waterways, it was always a wonderland for a kid like me. I loved this world so much that I named my first pet after it. My rabbit made quite a show at the county fair in his homey pen made by Papa Allister.

My nature time was and is my solace, my peace, my awakening. And time in nature seemed divinely planned. My father liked the out-doors too, so he would take me to the park, the woods, wherever nature grew. I believe it gave peace to him in the recesses of his mind.

His mind was a place I often dwelled, but on these days, I barely noticed, for in the woods, the grass, the breeze, I was alive and at home. Being alone with this pure, majestic world was just how I'd have it anyway. With and without him, I had the freedom for adventure, to explore and be and feel all that was, and all I was, with abandon.

I can still remember my imaginative fun. What I loved most to do in these woods up north was go frog catching. Sometimes, I imag-ined I was a Native American in moccasins walking at the water's edge. *How would they have kept the frogs from hearing?*

To those little frogs, I'd be a startling giant. *Fe Fi Fo Fum.* The ground probably shook with my every step! So, I made each one gentle and slow. I'd sneak up the shoreline of my favorite glass-wa-ter pond with ever-so-careful feet. Net in hand, I'd spot a pair of eyeballs or a muddy looking back across the water's surface, and in one swift swoop, Gotcha!

Every frog I caught went carefully in a watery pail to bring my proud catch of the day home to show Mom, and then set them free.

Now, what Mom thought was special about afternoons spent frog catching was that it was my dad's and my father-daughter time. But you see, Dad's idea of father-daughter time was this: We would drive through winding trails deep into 36,000 acres of wilderness to my favorite glass-water pond. We'd get out, and he'd coldly say over his shoulder, "I'll be back in a few hours." to little seven-year-old me and go off to take a hike. I loved it. I never fully acknowledged that this wasn't the order of things, perhaps because I liked it.

I guess I should have been scared all those times with the black bears, wolves, and cougars that roamed the woods. Not to mention the fact that we were next to a deep body of water, and I couldn't swim to save my life. Fear never once entered my heart. Alone with nature, my heart was too full to make room for fear. I was in my element.

Even more, I knew the unspoken rules of the forest. Be quiet so the predators won't notice you're here. Only go to the edge of the woods, never in. Looking back, I realize somewhere up above, or maybe deep inside, someone was looking out for me, impressing those knowings in my spirit.

One day, Dad decided to change it up and go somewhere different. He suggested Dollar Lake, a place on the map deeper into the woods than any other pond we could go.

"As long as it has frogs. Are you sure?" I asked. You never quite knew with his plans. And my glass-water pond had it all-caterpillars, beaver, all the prettiest trees. Scenes that made your heart catch.

"I think so. The lake should still be there." Should still be there!?!!

"Maybe we should just go to Three Mile . . ." Please. I could tell by the way he refolded the map that his decision was already made.

"We'll just find out. There's a pretty interesting landscape in that area. We'd better get going." He leaned over, scrunching his nose into his glasses, and peered out the sunny window. "It's a long drive back in there."

So off we set into the wilderness. Every section of the woods looks a little different. It's like there are neighborhoods of trees within the forest. There are groups of poplars with their shimmering, quivering leaves in two-toned green. The red pines standing tall with their canopies of needles above a hollow of smooth, red, uniform trunks you just wanted to leap out of the car and run through. I liked to imagine myself running through those trees with the deer, like friends sharing trust and silent beating steps across the coppery pine needles. Trust from nature was something I treasured.

Then, there were the birches with their white, peeling bark. I liked to call them paper trees because I would take the paper when it fell off and write notes on it to my mom in pencil. I still remember the joy I felt when she first taught me to do that. We left each other birch bark notes every year since, always signed with love.

We drove through the forest with the windows down, and I took in the cleansing scent of the woods, enjoying the silence between us so I could take it all in. And as we continued farther and farther, I began to wonder if we would even get there before dark. And though these woods were alright, I liked the path to Three Mile much better. It smelled better, showed more. But I just sat quietly and took in the ride.

Finally, the car slowed as we came upon a clearing. In the middle of this never-ending forest was a rolling meadow. What I didn't see was a pond. When we walked out into the middle of the meadow, we found a very large puddle sitting in the banks of what *used to be* Dollar Lake.

Dad seemed to have expected this, but was happy nonetheless. His hiking route awaited. I chose to be happy with the puddle. It looked deep enough for frogs to swim in, and it was enticing in other ways. So, I donned my frog net and made my way down to the banks.

"Okay . . . I'll be back in a few hours." Dad set off into the woods with his compass, leaving seven-year-old me alone. In the deepest piece of the 36,000-acre wilderness. By the water. When I couldn't float, let alone swim! Wildlife roamed plentifully through these woods, nature untamed. Of course, I thought of none of these things in this way. I was happy to be alone with nature. And I think nature was happy to be alone with me too.

I looked down at the remnants of what used to be the bottom of the lake. What remained was the scummy bottom-of-the-lake mucky mud. Like a ring around the puddle that remained of the water. *This mud is cool!!* I thought to myself as I stepped down the embankment, wishing I could go barefoot but knowing my mother would never approve. I thought somewhere in the world, a pig would have died and gone to Heaven for this mud.

Scoping out the best point of entry, I began to notice something on the ground all around me. Prints! *Somebody must have brought their dog here.* I looked left and right all across the mud. Large canine paws with large nails to match. Very large paws. Too large to be a dog. A *wolf! Maybe I'll get to see a wolf!!!* Now THAT *would be cool.*

But then the unexpected happened. I took my next step and that cool mud sucked my beach shoes right off my feet! *Careful what you wish for . . .* So there I was, carefully trying to place my feet back into my shoes without getting dirty . . . because I was a lady after all, I wasn't all tomboy. Suddenly, I was wholeheartedly grateful that my mother gave me protective shoes . . .

Because with the next step I took, I saw in the murky water what looked like a long, leopard-printed leech! Now, if you haven't experienced a leech, one you are a fortunate individual, and secondly, I would describe to you a leech as a swimming slug that latches onto your skin like a suction cup and sucks your blood. Gross, but not at all threatening when wearing mom's loving, protective beach shoes. I looked at it like you gaze at a python on the other side of the glass at the zoo. Half shivering horror, half secure fascination. What I didn't see were frogs. *Did the giant leech eat all the frogs?* No, that's not scientifically possible. But I couldn't help but wonder looking at that thing. Even the way it moved was creepy.

The other strange creature I met was a new kind of turtle. Most animals I met I became immediate friends with. It's like I knew how to react to them, and they just allowed me into their space. Not this lady. I tried talking to her, but she wasn't much for conversation. I pet the snapper on the back a few times and she didn't appreciate that much. She started hissing at me! I thought I'd better back off.

That was about the extent of the living creatures in this pond. I was not going to use my net today. I walked across to the other side of the pond to get another point of view. My eyes were fixed on the water, watching for a frog's head to be poised at its surface or its back at the edge. It wasn't until I looked down that I realized stretching out far and wide on either side of me, all across the mud, everywhere, I was surrounded by hordes of wolf tracks. WOW. *Maybe I'll get to see a wolf PACK!!* I gaped at the scene. Something grinded at the back of my mind telling me that this was a bad thing, but I shooed it away like a fly. Nature was my friend. I went right on back to exploring.

After hours had passed, the sun was dipping low in the sky, and I began to feel a growing awareness of time, an urgency. If dad didn't get back soon, we wouldn't make it out of the woods before dark. I did not like the idea of him driving these trails at nightfall. The woods felt very different by day than by night. We needed to get home.

I wasn't going to break my unspoken law. And in foreign terrain, I wasn't comfortable going to the edge of the woods. Late afternoon was turning to dusk. Animals would be more on the move near dusk. How I knew this I do not know.

I needed to stay here, especially in strange territory. So, I decided to go just to the crest of the hill to see if I could see him from there. If only I could find him and reign him back to course. If I couldn't see him, then I would decide what to do.

I looked up to the crest of the hill to take my first step toward it. Standing atop that hill were two wolves. I don't know how long they'd been watching me, but one *literally* licked his lips. My first thought was, *Darn it, I left the camera in the car!! If I run to get it, they'll get excited and eat me.* So, I just stood there frozen in awe of them and in respect for them because the fact was that my life lay in their choice. To eat me or not to eat me. Deep in this forest, nothing would stop them.

Picking up a rock, I banged it against my frog net. It was the only noise that could possibly weird them out without sounding like a scream or a growl which they'd take as a challenge. One looked at the other and at me. The other looked at his mate, then back to me again. And in one fluid motion, they sauntered back into the woods with that lopey wolf walk of theirs. Their choice left me in awe at the grace of God and majesty of nature once again.

I watched them till they disappeared. Half because I wanted to see every glimpse I could of this wowing experience, and half because I wanted to know exactly where they were. I wanted to be certain they weren't circling back around.

Maybe they thought I was too crazy to eat with those strange clanging noises. Maybe I was too small to be worth it. Perhaps it was divine intervention. All I know from that moment was that when a wolf stares you in the eye, he looks right through you, all of you. I wouldn't say that stare scared me so much as it made my spirit shiver. It gave me a respect for the beast and his kingdom. And, excited as I was, it made me miss my mom.

When I got back to Grammy's that night, I burst through the door. I could not wait to tell Mom what I saw. Dad, for some reason, looked a little sick. When I recounted my tale about my amazing experience, Mom was most interested in why I was not protected, how many times I was not thought of or cared for. Which led to the admission that on every father-daughter bonding trip we had taken in my young childhood, I was left alone by the water in the woods. That subsequently brought those trips to an end. I was sorry for their end, but I understood why they needed to. I saw his neglect wasn't right despite its gratifying gift of adventure.

Reflection: Viceroy

There are butterflies so like a monarch many can't know the difference. To the untrained eye, they look the same. To the trained eye, you can see the difference in the way they fly, a daring speed over the lilting flight. A narrow wingtip over the curve of the real thing.

It reminds me that in life and love there are sometimes ruses. We have to be privy to what's around us. Feel not just see. Know and hear. Every sense has something to tell us when we quiet ourselves and pay attention. Once we do that, the truth is plain for all.

Life: **Floating**

One day, I asked Dad to take me to the beach. So, off we went down the rocky cliff. Across the weedy stones, across the plank that bridged one side of the sandy beach to the other over the frigid icy stream until we made it to even ground. A good place to start. It was a smooth water day, and I'd been waiting all week for this to use my brand new inner tube to float. Mermaid Barbie was coming along with me for the ride.

I set my tube on the water, and boy it was a debacle getting in, but Mermaid Barbie and I finally got situated, and we set out to sea. Dad, he was wandering farther and farther away having said something about going to look over there. He was visibly bored with my activities. Somehow today, I felt a little uncomfortable with that, with water and all.

Floating, of course, was contained to shallow areas only because I could not swim. I mean, I couldn't doggy paddle. I'd taken swimming lessons not once but *twice* as a young child, which I admittedly still was to some degree, and I *still* couldn't swim. I couldn't even float! Deep water was a deep fear. Every so often, I dunked Mermaid Barbie underwater and used her to check that we were still in shallow waters. If her head touched the bottom, we were good.

I floated and relaxed. Mermaid Barbie swam over the top of the water because I didn't want to move too much and rock the tube. I must have had Mermaid Barbie and me on a sandbar because all of a sudden when I dunked her, there was nothing at the bottom . . .

Fear clenched the pit of my insides. I tried to paddle, but I didn't want to tip or slip. One wrong move and I was a dead kid. Gone without a sound. Just a floating inner tube. Horror filled me up. I tried just paddling with my hands because that didn't rock. But I could only paddle with one hand. I didn't want to let go of Mermaid Barbie because I'd need her to gauge whether I was back on safe waters. So, that one hand sent me paddling in circles . . . I couldn't save myself.

I suddenly realized one very important lesson about still waters on Lake Michigan. When there are no waves, the current is going out to sea. I was being taken out to the deep, and I just hadn't realized it being so near to the water's surface. Now, the shore looked impossibly far away.

The only thing I could do was call for help. And Dad was the only one out there, even though he wasn't in sight. So, I yelled. I yelled till my voice was starting to cut out. I yelled till I started imagining the sun sinking low in the sky and me still out there but instead without a voice. *Yikes.* I started taking breaks in yelling so that wouldn't happen.

I wondered about Mom, wishing she were close enough to hear, wishing she were here. I liked my freedom with Dad to explore and wander, but with her I was safe and loved. She always watched. Again, I yelled, this time louder than ever. And finally, he appeared from somewhere far away on the other side of the beach. He made his way calmly, cooly, slowly to my inner tube. The water was up to his chin. Imagine where it would have been on little me! I *would* have drowned. Here I was hoping it wasn't as deep as I thought!

He pulled me back in like a tugboat bringing me back to shore. A moment of relief and reassurance washed through me, and he pulled me back without exploiting my fear and vulnerable state. For the first moment, I felt secure in his care. But he did so mechanically, like he was still bored. "This really is deep." he said casually, more to himself than to me. "Why did it pull me out this far?" I asked, still trying to make sense of the shoreline that looked so close from the surface in my inner tube.

"Whenever there aren't waves, the water sucks you into the deep." he replied.

"Anytime there aren't waves it pulls you into deep water?" Did I understand him right? Did I hear him clearly? He knew.

"Yes. I thought about that when you were setting out." His back to me, I was glad he wasn't able to see my eyes. The hurt and horror draining through them would have prompted him to lash out at me.

Instead, he returned to his faraway wanderings as soon as I could touch bottom.

I can't describe the feeling that settled into my core as the waves flowed over my back. All I can say is that the feeling came back again and again through the years to come, just like those waves, until I understood that this was my father's nature.

I wanted to ask him why he didn't tell me, why he didn't look out, protect. But I knew it best not to. It never accomplished good to ask him why. He lashed out at questions like that.

I was equally washed with relief and instilled with a deep knowing that I was not safe with him. I never went out on the inner tube in calm water again. Not without Mom. I knew from that day forward, my dad consciously chose not to protect me from life.

He actively chose to let the dice roll as many times as opportunity arose. My truth was that I had to be conscious of the fact that I could not trust my father to keep me from harm. And when you realize that, what's to keep you from wondering if he would take it one step further and carry out the deed? Fantasy and reality can draw a fine line.

Now that I'm older, wiser, I see beyond fine lines. The freedom that comes from him not caring brought about the very change I needed, we needed. It allowed us to fly free.

Life: Masks

Though I love him, I'm keenly aware that there's a certain charisma to my father that only a few people know is a mask. It's so good that my most intimate of friends, even my family, were lulled in. With a chameleon-like persona, he held prestige among the rich and tapped an intellect for which only I could detect the ego that lied beneath. With those socially or fiscally below him in his eyes, he didn't care, unless it was on a public platform. With my brother, he boasted of political ideologies that mimicked his. Whichever way he could mirror a person so as to attain their deepest sense of brethren. Make a bond that went surface deep beneath the colors of his ever-changing skin and down to the heart of whichever companion was serving a purpose at the given time. The connections appeared so real, until the mask came off when the door closed.

We had an outwardly perfect household nestled in a community where he presented a model pillar. In the sights of others, he appeared to care for us so much in showy acts, until the door was closed. When others' eyes weren't around, the mask fell quickly off to reveal a man filled with brooding resentment. How I wished the mirage matched reality. Sometimes it was easier to try to believe that was true. But the truth is the best road to take; in the truth, there are no diversions.

Realities are hurtful to face sometimes when you don't want them to be true. Sometimes you wish you didn't see them, but you do. As painful as it was, I was grateful I didn't waste time living in a lie. I was painfully aware of his essence. I remember little time in my very early years when I wasn't aware, when I trusted him. Yet, as strong as I thought I was, as strong as I really was, I know deep inside how wounded I am. How I longed to connect with him so much I let myself be used and cast aside again and again and again. How I didn't *live* because of that need to be the strong one, always there. It was what I wanted to be. Deep within me, I needed to give an unconditional love no matter the conditions. I dreamed of that kind of love in return, in any semblance. I knew it existed because I felt it deep within me. My world, the world, needed more of it.

I don't share this story to attack my father; I say it to share for someone out there who may be alone in the same kind of way. I understand that kind of nature creates a reality that you are trapped in. Trapped between what appears and what is; what others believe and what you live. It was a life Mom and I relished in escaping from time to time so we could be free, be us. Live authentically. Even if just for a day.

Living in the lie of my father's visage took power away from both me and my mother, but with age comes wisdom. It didn't take me many years to realize that my father wasn't right. By the age of seven, I was writing "Daddy" under "Things that bother me" on those reflective school papers teachers have you write to reveal a child's endearing thoughts and features. By the age of eight, I told my mom that I wished she and Dad would get a divorce.

By twelve, I was waging a full-fledged effort to gently and respect-fully reform the way he did and did not treat my mother only to find that it made his wrath intensify and turn towards me. The psycho-logical warfare used at that time haunts me to this day if I let it. I learned that my love for my mom meant silence and control over my desire for what's right. I trained myself to hold back when the wrath of the workday no one else saw fell onto her. I took on the weight of his tactics as I was lured into the dynamic of earning love through his hate. Of feeling safe in the shifting sands of his temperament. Of trying to expect the unexpected. Of feeling the truth I did not see. His were the same tactics I saw when I got older, except at the age of twenty-six I was now equipped with the power of empathy, observa-tion, and will. I knew my way out. This time, manipulation didn't grip my freedom because I knew Love held true power.

We had more power than he ever realized, Mom and I. We found ways around it. Through Love. Love is consistent, persistent, and true. It's something to rest in and rely on.

Reflection: Faithful Flying

There's something magical about the way an eagle flies. My first Native American friend told me you can always tell an eagle by the way it flies. The shape of their wings in the sky is different from any other bird. Back then, I could only aspire to be so attuned. So, I practiced.

Today, I can spot a bald eagle from fields away. Rewarded for my practice, I understand exactly what he meant. An eagle doesn't just beat its feathers. It soars and glides through the sky. It's as if those wings are sails for the powerful ship that is its body, steering its course through the crystal blue light of the day, riding the shifting tides of the wind.

Perception holds the keys to our seeing what lies before us. When we see deeply, an eagle teaches us a lot through the way it flies. By passing glance, some could see a bird casually coasting through the day, looking down on its kingdom below. Others might see a wild one rising through the trees and up. It chooses not to press against the changing winds but rather rides them masterfully over the forest to take in the world from its view.

The winds of change are a dependable part of life and nature. The eagle is unlike many birds seen tumbling and rushing, pushing and flailing, going nowhere in the wind as they fight to carry on the route of their plan. No, the eagle, this force of nature, harnesses the push of the gusts. Without resistance, it meets the unstoppable might of the wind with the honed practice of its lift and coast, taking it to where it was best to land all along. In this elegant craft, eagles show us just how to glide through winds of change, no matter how gentle or roaring, with an awe-inducing grace.

Within each of us lies the potential to find this eagle. Imagine. Feel the wind blow all around your skin, your hair, in essence your feathers and your wings. It's riveting. It overcomes you with its energy, the power that is unstoppable and ever moving, body and spirit. It calls you to follow its flow, feel its shifts of change.

When you give rise to flight, you become a symbol of strength, courage, power, and freedom. It seems like that soar shows exactly how.

How it takes strength of character to rise above. But when you do, you certainly get a broader view of the forest when before you were lost in the trees. From those crystal blue skies above, you see even yourself more clearly.

How courage is required all for the leap off the branch, for once you're sailing the uplifting, shifting tides of the wind, something larger is at hand to show you the way. It soothes you, wakens you, empowers.

Wind may die low or surge through the sky, making you feel all alone in that vast crystal blue horizon. But you are not alone. You are never alone. For the same force that churns the air is guiding your course. Giving you everything you need to build deep from within.

The expression of all that you build is in your mastery of soaring; in your harnessing of the wind. Harnessing the power to set your own course, the right course, the one that follows the sense deep inside you. The sense that stirs you to speak, to move, to act, to still. Your power is seated in every great and tiny following of that sense. You feel it when you move.

As you move your way, I love your freedom most of all. Like the power of a vigilant soldier in the wake of sacrifice, or the valiance of a step through an unknown door, freedom is bred from faith. It's a faith in knowing that your wings are not the only things that fuel your course, that something omnipotent supports your greater way. Just like the wind, it blows below you, behind you, above and around, encompassing you in the love and force you need the most. Accept it, have faith in it, soar in it, for the freedom of flying comes from faith.

Through that faith, the eagle's freedom is found in a more all-encompassing way. It's found by the magnificent blend of power that can only be born from Grace. Grace gives you the small voice to hear, to feel, to know, to steer your course. It tells you the route to follow as you ride the wind. It sets your course with rest when you have no wind at all to push you. Power grows stronger each time you have the strength and the courage to follow your knowing. It grows more firmly seated alongside the growth of your faith in yourself, of your faith in God. And once you harness those skills, you discover that they were all connected, just as they have been within this bird.

So, what allows the eagle to soar so gracefully, unlike any other of its kind, is its willingness to give up its will. It shows a trust in the forces that guide it. It teaches us to remember that He'll carry you where you're meant to be how you were meant to go, so long as you harness the wind.

A few strong wing beats and it's on its way again. Like a team: the wind and the wings. When we harness life this way, through faith, no matter the weather, I believe we uncover the many dimensions of our inner eagle. We come to know that when we see that striking silhouette in the sky, there's something far deeper about their difference.

Life: Home

Now, home in my youth was not in the land of the pine. Those northern lakes and spirited woods were our great escape, a source of adventure and fuel for inspiration. Home was in a land sewn with crops: beans and corn. A place where small cities dwelled. My town was just that. It had a nice park where the prairie flowed like the waves of an ocean in late summer's balmy breeze. It's beech trees and maples gave a yellow hue to fall as their canopy sheltered my explorations.

I loved my old house. It was like living in history. With a creaky attic door and a floor that popped and groaned when you walked on it, the house spoke of its age. There were old fashioned lights and old-time doorbells that hearkened to the past, but most of all there was the roll of the brick street that still echoes in my ears if I close my eyes and open its place in my heart. There, I can see them shining in the rain, the smell of earth rising from the black dirt outside my window.

My old house wasn't perfect. It was drafty. The basement came straight from "Home Alone," complete with the smell. It even had nightmarish spider-looking crickets that threatened to jump on you when you ventured down there in the night. On summer nights I shared my bedroom vent with a squirrel who was busily crafting his entry into the house alongside the attic bats. The plaster walls were cracked, pipes drained slow, and the faucet often broke. But I loved it. I couldn't help but love it because it was the home of my memories, memories built on love.

Out of that leaky faucet, I remember bath time as a little girl. Being the nature child that I was, I loved frogs and lizards. When my bath wasn't filled with bubbles, making Santa faces or shaving off the bubbles from my legs, I had a water world of lizards and frogs that mom had especially for my bath. I'd play until I needed a warmup, my imagination and my passions tended to with love. Until it was time to wash me up and dry me off. Her warm smile matched the feel of her towel as she wrapped me up snug. To this day, I still think back to that comfort. It's the simple things we do every day for those we love that express the most, mean the most. Love is in the details. That's what my mother taught me about love.

Walks to and from school took place along those bricks as mom walked me to elementary school. Chats and discoveries along the way, sharing moments of each other's day. We shared everything because what we were was best friends, Mom and I. It's what we've always been. Love is constant and caring. My mommy taught me that too.

The kitchen was my favorite room. Cooking together was an art that reminded me just how well we worked together and made me feel like I was a good help. That feeling always meant a lot to me. But more than anything, time with Mom meant the most.

We'd play with Beaver the puppet, Barbara and Katherine the Barbie dolls, and Rick and Sam the raccoons who all had their own voices and went on adventures together full of spontaneity and laughs, just like Mom and me. Fun was a key ingredient of life well lived. I learned this from her too.

My mother taught me the value of hard work and generosity by example and first-hand experiences that made those values my own. She gave me a love of learning by challenging and enriching my mind in places school did not. She sculpted my character and cultivated my joy. I don't think I realized at the time that not all kids had that abundant kind of love, but I sure knew I had the best mommy in the whole wide world. She was my sunshine. When she was my world, there were no grey or cloudy days.

I remember one afternoon playing Polly Pocket on the living room floor. An understanding struck my mind. I want to enjoy playing with my toys and pretending because someday I'll grow out of this. I won't be a kid anymore. My mind will think differently, in a grown-up way' I sensed that someday the natural shift in the seasons of life would close my child's mind. Growing up would be regretful, yet changes like those were natural, necessary.

Those thoughts came to me from time to time, not mournfully, but in a way that made me live my season of youth with value, gratitude. Each experience was once-in-a-lifetime: a curious exploration outside, creative imagining indoors, precious moments with mom. I took them in with all of myself.

Life happens in seasons. They come and they go, and they don't return again. Each one is precious. Some are pure. Some are painful. Some are a mixture of everything in between. Every one serves an intentional purpose. As the seasons of our lives pass from one on to the next, they create the metamorphosis that is our lives. When we invest our whole selves into the season we are in, we live it to its fullest. Enjoy our loveliest happy moments. Feel most deeply our painful sorrows. Understand the truths of human existence that connect most every living thing. And in that same breath, while we are *living*, we become the fullest self we can be.

I do well to remember the seasons in life, precious, purposeful, perhaps eloquently both, and how they go by.

My mother fostered my passions, and one was my heart for butterflies, encouraging Dad to help too. In my childhood, I knew every type of butterfly by name, spending nights devouring books in fresh pjs and slippered feet. Stacks she'd carefully handpicked from the library shelves were born from hours of perusing the aisles for stories with just the right food to nourish my growing heart and mind. Though butterflies were a passion all my own, it seems my lifelong love for reading came from my mother's love for me. Love fuels the heart, the mind, the spirit. It builds you and makes you come alive all at once. That's my mother's love for me.

Life: **Metamorphosis**

By tradition, when we'd arrive up north, I'd peer closely among the plants for tiny yellow and black striped crawling creatures. I gathered Monarchs from the time they were caterpillars the size of a thumbnail on the banks of Three Mile Pond, bringing them back to the cottage in a well-crafted crate I'd fancied "The Butterfly House" in my great-grandfather's woodshed. Bringing these small creatures in was no small whim. It was a commitment, one I eagerly took on with great love and resolve. Every two days for a month, I set off into the woods in search of a specific plant to nourish their growing bodies: milkweed. And over the weeks, my caterpillars, whom I named of course, grew longer and fatter and ate more every day. I took them out in the lawn to get sun and roam free, guarding them against birds and lawn chairs (yes lawn chairs were a hazard too).

Then it would be time to go home. I'd find a secure place in the car for my caterpillars to make the long trek to Illinois. Being native to our state as well, I had no qualms about crossing them over state lines. If nothing else, I was shortening their migrational journey back to Mexico come fall. Finding milkweed in Illinois was a bit more of a challenge, but only for a short time because then came time for my youngsters to make their cocoons. I would find sticks for them to anchor on for their long and dormant stay. Placing their house in a cool, quiet spot, I'd allow them space to rest. My doting would have to subdue to small peeks in upon their lime green chrysalis with its gold seal. Several days later, usually in the wee hours of the morning, that lime green would turn crystal clear, a sure sign that the transformation was complete and what was once a lanky caterpillar was about to emerge as a regal Monarch. I watched in admiration and love as they fanned their wings on the shell that once protected them from the world as they changed into full form. And once they were dry and strong, I placed them on a flower and off they flew. Out into the world to enjoy the breeze that carries them.

Their metamorphosis, life, and rebirth; appreciating the beauty and full transformation of the butterfly is something I have long observed and respected. That metamorphosis would transpire for me in an essence of love and truth and faith, of friendship and letting go. All things that magically go hand in hand, no one without the other. And yet somehow, it seems the caterpillar requires them too inside its great little journey inside that lime green, gold sealed cocoon.

Life: **Fixing**

When I was young, I observed. I observed nature. I observed my family. I observed my life and how I was living it. For all the love my mother poured into me, she was equally giving to my father in caring for him the way he needed to be loved. Patience when he was angry at the world. She steered him back to center even when that meant that wrath turned onto her. She cared for the home in a way that cared for his needs as much as my own. Freshly preparing the meals he preferred each night, ironing his clothes, organizing his socks, being certain his oil was changed and the car was filled with gas, the garbage was taken, the lawn was mown. She did it all.

As a small child, I observed my mother's infinite acts of love. I also observed the way that my father depleted her. But it wasn't just that. My father spitefully, angrily took personal offense to the request that he take out the garbage when she'd had surgery. Or when a meal was cooked that he didn't prefer. When he liked dinner, he'd sit waiting for mom to fix his plate as he ranted about his enemies of the day. Then, he'd push it away for her to clear the table and do the dishes when he was done. Off to read the paper and watch the news that would inevitably feed his political temper. It was almost as if he thrived on animosity between two sides. Him against his coworker, against politics, against mom. As long as he found an opposing side, he was enlivened. Empowered by the needless resentments he held onto.

What's more was that he didn't seem to respect her many acts of love. It was as if they were an expectation that was never acknowledged for what they were, not appreciated, least of all returned.

It hurt me to see my mom mistreated. More than that, it violated the values I held dear and the person I held most dear. I wanted to make it right. When I was young, perhaps because I was young, I felt like I could. Gently, carefully, respectfully, I tried to guide him to the light. Show him the better way to treat my mother, the positive way to look at life. I tried with all my might because I thought maybe he didn't know better, and maybe he needed that.

I was wrong. He knew well my intentions. It was choice that held him back. His words still ring in my memory. "Clone," he called me, never by name. "Have you ever heard of Yin and Yang?"

"Yes." I replied, confused.

"Well, that's you and me. You're the Yin and I'm the Yang. You're the positive. I'm the negative." I can still see the smirk take up his lip, glinting his eye as a dark cast of enjoyment played over his face, adjusting himself in his chair with satisfaction. He'd known what I was doing, and at that moment, it dawned on me what he was doing too. Maybe he'd toyed with my emotions all along. But for him, this had become far more than the game. In his heart, I was now amongst his enemies.

Life: Path Choosing

The more I pressed on in building character and his heart with understanding, the more he shifted in an unexpected way. His apathetic coldness toward me had morphed into plain hatred. His eyes would enliven. A black would turn in them that let me know there was evil in him that could come out at one wrong word or intonation, action, or even his own unprovoked thought. His resentment for authority had turned toward me for showing him another way, for guiding him. Because he already knew the other way. He was making a choice.

His obsession in hating, villainizing me became so intense that I ultimately had to give up my mission to fix our home. Merely being who I was had become a threat that he competed with and thwarted at every turn. When he couldn't feel he beat me at life, he hated me more. He hated that I got good grades. He hated that people in the community respected me. He hated that I served others with a full heart. He hated that I exercised more than he did. He hated that I wanted him to respect Mom while at the same time I respected him. As I remained myself, he resented me more. He expressed it when we were alone through the undercurrents of his energy toward me. He expressed it in subversive statements nearly every single day. I couldn't help but feel the put-downs. They hurt because they came from my dad. At the time, I didn't see how I internalized it all, in a sense of not valuing who I was and what I did. It was as if his assertions and denials clouded my self-image.

I thought love could change that dynamic. I thought patience could change him. I believed that if I had faith and held onto it, that with time, his heart would be found, that he would love me, that he would feel my love for him. In my youthful eagerness and yearning, I thought I had the power to heal something inside my father that only he could touch within himself.

The more I tried to help, the more contempt he expressed for me in his morning conversations with mom, with fervency and obsession. She became caught between two people she loved. Two senses of home.

I felt the sense that he was taking it out on her because he knew that would stop my efforts, and it worked. If mom was going to suffer more when I tried to help, and she wasn't going to leave him, then things just were better off as they'd been. I realized that I had to stop trying to love and infuse positivity and respect into someone who wasn't accepting it...I had to accept him.

It was a struggle for me to temper my love into a sacrifice of morals and will. I learned how to keep a sense of grace between Dad and me by playing along, assuaging his ego. Placating his ideas was like applying a balm to the home for us all. Our home found peace by means of my sacrifices. And so, I made them every day. For her.

Life: The Force of Will

Accepting that I couldn't help didn't come easy. It was hard to give up this mission I was impassioned for. I was torn between knowing things weren't right and seeing I couldn't make them right for her. Accepting my powerlessness to help them tore me from the inside out. As I worked on giving up, I couldn't bring myself to enter the room when he was ranting and treating her disrespectfully. I couldn't watch him treat her like service and play sport with her feelings without doing something to help. I wanted to care for her. I wanted to be true to myself. I wanted to make it right. I wanted to show him what love really meant, to reach past these unnecessary circumstances. But I had to learn that changing this was beyond my will. A person can only change oneself. Changing him was not in my power.

It was incomprehensible to me, that he didn't want love and happiness, no matter how much I tried to reach him. How could he not want to feel good inside? Let alone spill that onto others? He was aware of himself, and yet he didn't want to improve within. The inner path of resentment was what he seemed to have chosen long ago, and that choice led him to cower in disgust at my affection. It led to disregarding our needs. Led to choosing spite, choosing to not respect. Ultimately, he'd chosen resentment over love. And as that choice became a pattern, that pattern had become etched into him.

Great power is held in the making of choices. When we meet adversity, we may choose to resent them or to love in the face of them. The former choice shuts our hearts down, spreads harm into oneself and onto others. The latter deepens the heart, expands it, makes it even more tender than before. When we choose to love through adversity, it is difficult, but we are rewarded for our inner efforts with the strength of knowing love, of knowing God. That strength expands the reach of love in your life beyond the comprehension of man.

Reflection: Soul Choice

We all face trials in our lives, some more or less than others. Some turn to God; the light. Others turn to hate. Therein lies one of the mighty powers of free will that keep us in an ever winding circle of life being learned freely, openly, with equal and binding force. The moment we release ourselves is the moment we are free again. Yet the moment we are free, we are once again bound to the never ending journey that is life rising and deepening evermore in its balance of order and grace. Always with the power of will.

Every season of life calls in a different kindness. It's our exceptional purpose to recognize it and then spread it around the corner of the world that calls to our soul.

Life: Where You Plant Your Heart's Seeds

As I mastered the skill of supporting his ego, my dad forgot he hated me enough that I could try to have a relationship with him. When I was young and naive, I'd forget his hatred too. My choice to submit made me lose touch with what was best for us. I picked up his slack in the home, in mom's heart, and I accepted what was. I lost touch with my anger and the confidence of my will.

For many years, I didn't give up on my dad. I tried with faith to connect, and I saw promise in the neutralized moments between us that my trying created through the years. I'd extend a helping hand or reach out to calm him, and in those moments, he felt kind or spoke to me conversationally. I would carefully trust, open up my heart again and again; believe I'd broken through. I believed he loved me. I thought he felt my love for him.

When I gave, like when I helped him with his work each week-end of my sophomore year of high school, he was pleasant. He even interacted and shared his thoughts with me in a way that felt like a relationship was growing between us. I felt a valued connec-tion, even if it hurt to be valued for what I could do for him. Yet all it would take was that one wrong word, at one wrong moment, even a mistaken tone, and the house of cards I'd carefully built between us would obliterate, as if they were never there. Beats of hatred surged into my core as his eyes turned black in an instant, threatening, but most of all cold.

The removal of peace was as cold to my teenage self as it had been to my young self. It felt like love being taken away. What I had yet to accept was that love cannot be taken if it was never there. And for that I felt like a fool each time for having hoped or believed it was real that time. It stung like hot tears that welled but did not spill after he'd stormed from the room and it was empty and silent and safe once again. His niceties, the mirage of his love that I wanted but told myself I didn't need, they were given under conditions. They were not consistent. They were not real. I learned so much from that. I learned that wasn't love.

It took me years to realize, *no rather to accept*, that his congeniality flipped to a harsh end the moment I wasn't of use anymore. It took me many, many times over to *accept* it. I had to accept the fact that my relationship with my father was turmoiled with conflicted feelings, mixed signals, competition, and hate, and that wasn't going to improve. It was hard to resist trying because I wanted to share love with my dad. Bit by bit, though, I was seeing the truth that it wasn't just that he didn't love me but rather he resented and wished me harm.

Life: The Power Threat Implies

Threats can come in many forms. Indirect and subversive, they send a signal to the inner cords of our senses that stay with us. They create a feeling that resides in the presence of a person that often cannot be revoked. Words matter. So does energy. Mind them. For their exchange sets the precedence for a relationship.

On my way out the door on a sunny day, he'd say to me, "Don't get sleepy driving." in a cold tone. "Don't get hit by a semi." with an alluring voice. "You might drive off the road." with cool nonchalance. "That happens sometimes."

Then came time for the proposed high school trip to Mexico for Spanish class. "You know, blonde haired, blue-eyed girls get raped and killed never to be seen or heard from again in Mexico. About 20% of them never return when they go on trips. I think you should go. You'd practice your Spanish and probably enjoy it." Needless to say, I didn't take the trip. I didn't know what to think about his words, but I knew how I felt. Wanted dead.

When I'd step out to take a bath, he'd tip the newspaper just enough to say, "Don't drown." a touch of satisfaction in his adjustment in his seat. "You know, you can drown in an inch of water." in the most serious and least sarcastic of tones.

All of these words he said to me over the years held a hue of subversive threat that communicated what wasn't said. They communicated to me that, in his mind, ideally I would die in a perchance kind of way, and he'd not be blamed for it. Instead, he'd be smirking in satisfaction as the sympathy washed over him from the community. This truth too, I silently lived with. Watched out for with diligence.

He feasted on fear. What he didn't see was that I wasn't afraid of him. People who threaten others that way require awareness. I was aware that through fear, my father wanted power over me, over my emotions. I knew not to tempt fate. I knew not to allow opportunities for which I was vulnerable near him. I knew he'd be the one to trip me if we were standing on a cliff. But each time he suggested all those threats, I rolled my eyes inside because he didn't have the power of fear over me.

Reflection: Burls

Burls. From the outside, burls are not much to look at, large bulging knots in a tree. But from within, they appear as rich colorful swirls that create beauty within. Burls are so sought after by people that when seen on a tree in the woods, a man may cut down the tree and strap it to the top of his car to take home for the makings of a work of art. For some, a table, others a coaster, a sign, anything to be admired. It's a source of awe, inspiration, and admiration.

I see two burls on my way to work each morning. They hold up the mailbox of a home on the highway. Each time I pass it by and notice, I think of the cost. When we admire the inner beauty of these burls, do we ever truly know the painful process a tree goes through to attain it? How a beetle bores into its healthy trunk to tunnel through its insides, creating complex tubules and designs only the beetle knows, and of course the tree? That the tree struggles to grow and bulges under stress in all its dying, trying effort to overcome, to heal, and mend?

But we admire the damage. We see it as a trophy. Why is that? If we really knew what it went through to get that beauty within, would we see it the same way? Or is it our ignorance that makes us believe so. I hope that knowledge would change our perspective. Or at the very least, honor it in a more reverent, merciful way. Because mercy on a tree who's tried so hard is something I believe it deserves above all others. For it has triumphed above all.

Burls exist only in some people. Like their presence on a tree, they outwardly appear the same color as the rest, except they show as a deformity of sorts on the trunk. Most people pass them by with a curl of the lip, the recognition of something seen as ugly, something natural but not. But what I see in these trees are human burls of inner triumph.

Those who have had an infestation into their hearts. One they've had to overcome much like this tree. Their bark does not differ from the rest, just like the tree. They've had to twist and compress inside, creating new colors and forms inside richer than one could imagine, just like the tree. They have overcome and live healthily, just like the tree. Some are judged for their ugly bulge, their difference, just like the tree. Others are respected for the magnificent beauty that lies beneath the bulging, seemingly normal surface because someone strikingly similar recognizes what's inside. Some are used for it, just like the tree.

But unlike the burled tree, inside a person that beauty, the rich swirls of color, a compression of passion. A passion that when channeled outward rightfully creates the beauty and change we need so desperately and most of all in this world. The kind of passion that touches the soul of another because it taps into the deep. Because the density of the fiber of the burl is representative of the depth of heart, the capacity for love and feeling that one has for being human. That only comes from walking the hard road over ashes of destruction within wounds of heartache overcome inside the bark. Confined inside the outer walls of normalcy until the right time and condition comes to express the true beauty that lies within. The true nature of the burl is an inner passion and depth and self creation that comes from inner torture harnessed by the contrast of dark and light, channeled into light and love and something greater than oneself. Something that can change the world for someone else. Something for those passersby who can recognize the beauty in the burl.

Life: Contentment

My childhood sounds unique. I realize that as I place pen to paper. Yet I look back on my youth as the happiest years of my life thus far. What made all those feelings of danger and lack livable was that Mom and I had each other. When I was still a child, I opened up to her about how I felt toward Dad; about his relationship with us and the world and how different that was.

At first, she seemed surprised by how vividly I saw into him. I think I affirmed the things that she'd felt. In time, we became more than mother and daughter. We were each other's confidants when we needed someone to understand. We lifted each other up. We made each other laugh, shared one another's sorrows, tended and cared. We took care of one another in the ways we needed. Sometimes in the form of long evening talks, most others in the form of a shopping trip or bedtimes laughing ourselves to sleep being silly. We dreaded when that clock would roll around to the time when Dad should come home, but most often, we found reprieve in the love we shared for each other. We made the best with what we had, and in my mind, my mother loved me more than most children got to have from both their parents. I look back on my youth and smile. Because of her. In my heart, I couldn't ask for more.

Reflection: God's Work in Milkweed

A weed can be a flower of sorts. A lot of things, I believe, are defined more by a person's perspective than what they really are. Milkweed, for instance, is the only plant that feeds the monarch caterpillar. In late spring, rosy purple flowers bloom from tall stems that fuel the regal ladies before they lay their eggs on their broad leaves. Then, when her babies emerge no larger than the length of your fingernail, the milk within those leaves fuels them to grow to just about the size of your whole finger. Making their gold-sealed cocoon on that very plant to emerge weeks later, fanning wet wings to dry in the early morning sun. In the second World War, children collected pods to make flotation devices that saved soldiers' lives in combat. All this life-giving might in what we unwittingly regard as a weed.

History in mind, I came upon these plants on my late autumn walk. As I saw them from a distance, they looked like a white wisp of granny's hair atop a browning stalk so blackened it looked burnt. A far cry from the vibrant colors of spring, but yet they took center stage against the backdrop of the roadside.

In late autumn, when the case of a milkweed pod cracks open at the seam, it reveals a nest of silk-bound seeds inside. As I peered inside, there was something about them that took my breath away. Every single seed was arranged inside that pod in neat, tidy rows, like someone carefully packed them in there. Each silky puff was bound to the stalk at their tip so that as the pod unfolded, they opened up like synchronized swimmers in formation. Like little stars ready to blow away in the wind. God takes great care in putting even the smallest seed pod in order. And there's an art to the way it unfolds and lets go, ready to begin again. So many affirming truths in one mighty weed.

Life: Release

One afternoon, Mom asked, "What would you think about us taking a girls trip?" I was 13. I'll never forget the whirl of thrill I had when those words passed Mom's lips. Her idea sparked a chain of change. Upon my father's authoritatively dismissive approval, we packed our bags and planned our route. Our first time was in June. The drive was as great as the destination.

It was a good thing I was comfortable in my shotgun seat by Mom. If either one of us wanted to make any adjustments, we were tempting the odds of an avalanche. Our old Buick was filled to the gills. Somehow, no matter what resolutions we made each summer to downsize or compact our parcels, we always managed to find ourselves strategizing to merely maintain enough window space to see out the rear! For all the tender loving care she kept it with, mom's nine-year-old car still smelled new, and it made the nine hour journey we were embarking on a comfortable ride. Within arm's reach sat a small cooler that held the delectable comforts of Momma's cookin', a warm grilled sandwich and chips with rice crispy treats made just hours before. Always a special "surprise." When enroute to the home of the heart, there is no time for pit stops. We ate on the road.

Absorbed in the sounds of Motown and Soul, I gazed out the passenger window at the view whirling by us. Prairie grass whipped to and fro up the hills of the viaducts like flowing ocean waves, small parcels of land showing a glimmer of the grace of the Cornbelt's natural past. As we passed on into Wisconsin, antique silos with their old iron rod grate-topped with cone shaped tin roofs still held corn doing their jobs as they did an era ago. They stood aged but proud, just as they should be next to the barns straight from the pages of a Billy Jacobs calendar. These scenes of calm cattle grazing in pastures and old schoolhouses turned into homes brought comfort to two old souls embarking on adventure.

In a small manila folder, the keys to the city awaited us. I'd hop out of the car to retrieve #34 and away we went down the road. Rolling down the window, the rich smell of pine soothed my soul. The vast sky touched my spirit. Our humble abode was just that, humble. Our happy place was an outdoorsman's world really. Through a cloud of hungry mosquitoes, we'd unpack the car, carrying our things into our small rental cabin. Turning the key with its orange numbered tag, the smell of bleached floors hit us before we stepped through the door. We'd clean and add comforts. Sheets over the old dusty armchairs long covered in hair of hunting dogs past. Taping the bathroom screen that invariably fell out at some point in our stay. By the time our tablecloth was draped and the twinkle lights awaited the night, the place was our own. Perfect for just us two.

With such small quarters, we spent a lot of time outdoors. There was a small swing out the front door that I loved no matter how many years passed. I loved how in the simple act of swinging, I felt like I was swooping right to another realm of joy and peace. Swinging felt like childhood. One time, when mom was on the stoop watching me, dark clouds came rolling in. The thunder cracked, and just like that, we were outrunning a rainstorm as it blew in across the lake. Those large drops pelted our ground just as our feet made it inside the doorstep, skirting the back of my shirt. It's a wonder we made it in for the moment we wasted standing in awe and the weakness in our running legs from laughing so hard.

Being independent women who weren't much for making big campfires, we'd make s'mores over the coil of our electric apartment-sized stove. We'd polka dance together through the small one room living space on a rainy afternoon over the public broadcasting channel out of Wisconsin, trying to teach ourselves and always ultimately having more fun just winging it. We took joy in the simple things, just the two of us.

Over the years, we got braver in our route, taking on the unknown a little more and finding the right fit for gas and a good night's stay. We also learned the dos and don'ts of being an up-north resident. Like "Don't buy meat at the local market." One week, I got a particular hankering for Momma's fried chicken and gravy. Back before weight control was even something I paid mind to. We rode off into town to get ourselves an innocent package of chicken and stop at the mailbox.

Stepping into the local grocery store was like stepping into a portal back in time. The well-worn floorboards groaned beneath my feet and my nose filled with a nostalgic scent of dust and old that only sentimentalists would appreciate. We knew to shop the perimeter of the store because the center aisles held the dry goods. No telling what the expiration dates may be on those. But their bread, milk, bananas, and sorts were staple moving goods. We figured chicken must be the same if inspected.

After checking out, we went next door to mail some postcards to family. Minutes later, when we opened the car door, the most pungent odor filled our noses. "What IS that?!" It was the chicken. In daylight, it was green. Lesson learned: Shortcuts aren't worth it. Always buy chicken at Walmart, no matter how many hours away! The same applied to veggies and fruits. The fact was in the north woods you had to plan ahead. Supply trucks were lucky to make it up here while the items were still fresh. Many arrived just before molding.

It's true, this place didn't have a lot. It was simple, even isolated. And we were happy with that because like the old country tune, we were living on love. Mom and me.

Our trips together breathed a whole new life into us, a sense of freedom and joy that couldn't be held back. It gave us a place to live life wide open, free-Willy, all-in. Weeks before each trip, months really, I made a paper chain to count down the days until we left. The shorter it got, the more our anticipation built. What else built over the years was a growing feeling there of coming home. Inside, what I was really doing was coming home to myself in that land.

Life: **Peace of the Night**

I wish I could send a bottle of the night air to you. Earth and cedar and pine and life breathes into your lungs in one crisp breath of quiet freshness. Not a sound but the water lapping and the toads croaking softly in the forest. So peaceful. I can barely tear myself away to go to bed.

Life: Dreaming

When I was a young girl sailing across those drives up to what was becoming the home of our hearts, I used to dream of what love would be like. As I watched the rolling grassland and corn fields in the flat lands of Central Illinois whirl by, I'd spend long car rides getting lost in the melodies and lyrics of romantics and song. Little did I know that as the years unfolded of my life, those romantic ideals would be put to the test in ways I never fantasized. Some discouraging, some downright comical, and others darker than I care to revisit. Experience would change me and teach me step by step what love looks like in our modern world, or perhaps in its timeless form. There were many lessons in love I just knew inherently, for an old soul knows who she is and what she wants. But those years ahead of me would teach me what I didn't want and what I stood for. Most importantly, those hard roads would show me so many things about people and myself that would bring me home within myself to stay. I just didn't know it yet. In all its forms and measures, life is a lesson in love to those watching and listening to learn. But for now, I was happy to be a simple young girl, living a chapter that I chose to be for myself and my life. This was a time not for romance but for dreams, for life, in all its many other forms to be lived, savored.

Reflection: The Barn

On our route to and from our favorite place, there are certain landmarks that punctuate how far we've come, how far we have to go. There's a bond that forms with these places just for the anticipation of seeing them as we travel our long, loved road.

It is the unique places that stay with me. Those places that are in essence, a form of expression, like the silo in the shape of a jack-o-lantern, or a cobalt blue barn in tribute to the dairy farmers 'round America.

But some places haunt me. They stick in my spirit. There is a barn on the highway that stands in disrepair. Holes in the roof. Boards broken in its walls. The structure was clearly falling apart. Someday, piece by piece, it will fall into the ground, a memory. History.

But when you consider the boards and shingles, the letters that adorn its front face, the cupolas resting atop, you envision it in all its glory. You fill in the pieces of its unknown past to sculpt together the story yet untold. It's a mystery of your making.

What will remain in my memory long after the image of its prime, beyond the time it falls down to the earth, what remains in my mind's eye, in my heart, are those holes in the roof where the light shines in. It makes me wonder at how there wouldn't be this flood of light in that old forgotten barn without its dilapidated hole. Just like the holes and cracks in our hearts are where the light pours in, without that "damage," there'd be no opportunity to fill that space with the bright effervescence of light. The Light that is Love in all its purest forms from Heaven.

What stays with me are those cracks in the walls, the gaping spaces that allow creatures in. Who knows what lives in that barn? But who knows what that barn gave a safe place to lay? To stay? Because walls aren't everything. And letting in isn't so bad. Sometimes, the creatures that made their way inside make a hollow place turn to home.

Those letters, some in place, some gone, some hanging on a nail. They tell a story of another time. I'll let your imagination fill in the details. Use the senses. Take your time. Explore the great unknown.

Lastly, there's the osprey who faithfully return to raise their young each year. To them, no time has passed. They've perched atop the cupola on that barn roof just as their parents who came before them. They've repaired their nest through the storms that put a hole in the roof. Tended their young as the boards cracked below. For this place is as traditional to them as it is to us. They knew this barn before it became old. They lived over it before we ever came. They depend on that barn and its cupola. And maybe, somehow, that barn, in all its times and stages, depends on those birds too. Perhaps it even looks out for us.

So you see, within the breaking of things lies the great opportunity for new light to pour in. From God above, from nature, from people in even the unlikeliest of places, from those we count on most, even from the mysteries.

Man may leave the barn to fall in disrepair, but God never leaves you. He always makes a way. Never ceasing to fill holes of sorrow and use a crack to bind souls in synchronicity. Sewing the tapestry of our lives ever interwoven in magic and mystery. His work of art that keeps us ever in wonder. What a grand design. Isn't that a way of Love?

Life: Bentley

Among their many highly attuned senses, perhaps the most powerful awareness that animals have into our lives is a keen intuition for being there for us exactly when and where we need them most. I've known the kismet of their graceful spirits stepping into our lives at just the right moment in the perfect way so much that when it happens, I've come to wonder if some have signed up for the role of being a healer clothed in fur.

To this day, Bentley's friends and family speculate with one another as to whether an easy-going tabby cat with its friendly disposition wandered into Bentley's yard one day with that knowing in its bones or if one especially well-meaning friend knew that Bentley's grief had taken him to a place where his most beloved friends could not reach him. His large and generous heart was truly broken. What was once the kind, happy man they knew had turned to what resembled a grumpy old farmer closed off to the world.

That was the man I met, one whom I barely knew when I first ventured over to pet the big tabby cat lazing in the fresh summer's day across the road from our rental cabin. A nature lover all my born days, I was tickled and delighted to find that cat. What I didn't realize was the gift of friendship she was inviting me over to unfold.

At first, it started as a short word here and there, but as care deepened, the visits lengthened. It was a beautiful friendship shared with him through the years. Memories I never want to forget, simple times when I would walk over to swat mosquitoes off my arms and legs for an hour just to chat with him in his garage as he tinkered away.

Sometimes he was taking on projects for others, like mowing his daughter's yard well into his eighties. He'd take a rubber mallet to his rotted riding mower tires because he could get another year out of them. A conservative sentiment he probably garnered from growing up in the aftermath of the Great Depression.

Other times it was simple projects, like laying out his wooden boardwalk that led from the garage to the house, something I imagined was a habit he carried on in honor of his wife and her wish to keep the sand at bay in their old cabin's carpeting.

I was convinced that tinkering was what kept him young. His hard working ethics driven by a joyful, light spirit gave him a vitality many men lacked at half his age. In those conversations and moments with him, I studied his neatly combed white hair, his clean-shaven cheeks that sagged with age, somewhat dated glasses that suited him, his wrangler blue jeans and white tennis shoes, tanned arms from working in the sun, the way his shoulders shook up and down as he laughed, something he did so easily, most often at his own jokes which erupted me into tickled laughter right along with him. I took in every special moment with him, my chosen extra grandpa. I loved him like that, and his generous care showed me that he cared for me too. He had his own family and grandkids to adore, but he had a place for me too.

Bentley had a great place in his heart for loons. Loons adorned his cabin, and he kept a pair of binoculars at the picture window of his living room for the off chance that one might swim by. So that he could get a good look at the starry night sky on their back, the crescent moon on their neck. A Native American totem that speaks, "Love lives on forever."

It wasn't until I visited with his daughter one rainy afternoon that I learned what that loon meant. "Oh, loons are Mom. Whenever we hear them or spot them out on the lake, we know it's her."

One of those summer days as my mother and I visited him on his gray wooden porch, he took a moment's pause, looked me straight in the eyes, and shared with me heartfelt advice I will never forget, "You need to find a man who worships the ground you walk on." his arms spreading wide to emphasize that ground. He meant every word, and the love he shared with his wife embodied that. He wanted nothing less for me. I carried those words in my mind through the years I searched for love. I may have forgotten to follow them sometimes, but I never once forgot the way it felt to have a man care enough to want that for me.

I knew he'd given that kind of love to his own wife for all the years they had together because I could see it in his eyes when he spoke of Katherine. Hear it in his voice as he told of the time he had her take flying lessons for her birthday just so she could feel empowered and independent. How she would accompany him on his business trips selling Harvestore grain bins. I could feel the joy they had in sharing one another's company, so much so that she wanted to ride along just to be with him. And he wanted to have her there, right by his side.

On one of those trips, Katherine went shopping while Bentley was in a sales meeting, and got her heart set on a davenport. Of course, at a small cabin on the lake, a piece of this size would never fit through the door, and she was alright with that. But Bentley wanted her to have it. So he bought her that sofa, and he removed the living room picture window for its delivery, just so she could have that piece she loved so much. Sharing joy in her joy. And giving her the best. The joy he felt from her happiness was strong long after she was gone.

His stories melted my heart, and I could see that she was a reflection of his joyful, giving heart. I wished I could have met her. But her loss was one of many heartbreaks Bentley had experienced in his years of life. One summer, when they were up north, her pacemaker punctured her heart. Being so far north, it took nearly two hours to get to a major hospital. She simply couldn't be gotten to the hospital in time. It pained me to imagine him behind the wheel on that anxious drive, knowing those could be the last moments with his love, that they were doing the best they could. That incredible loss was the reason for the grumpy old man I'd been shy to when we'd first met. When Bentley lost his Katherine, he stepped into a shell. And I couldn't know he was inside.

What else I didn't know was how much his life's stories would touch my heart and my memory to empower my own work for the children who came into my classroom.

As I grew up to be a teacher, Bentley's life story became something I tell to my students every school year, not for his love, but for his younger years. Many of my students come from a background that imparts them with heavy emotional burdens and deprives them of many of the things that I was so blessed to receive from my mother. Things like learning how to love and be loved, show compassion and receive it, knowing their worth. These things I seek to teach them. Watching the fruition of my love for them is what fulfills my heart in my profession.

Bentley holds within him a powerful lesson that I wish everyone could hear. Because though not everyone can be so touched as to know him, they could at least learn a very valuable lesson from the way in which he's lived his life.

Though we look back on long ago eras with a sense of idealism that makes us imagine model families and homes, people are people, and time doesn't alter their nature. When Bentley was born back in 1930, it was unclear whether his mother was unable or unwilling to care for him and his brother, but nonetheless, they were placed in foster care. Occasionally, she came to visit them, and in those visits, as if guilt had stricken her for the moments she faced her own flesh and blood, he and his brother heard promises from her that she was either never able or willing to keep. Able or willing? A question that haunts the hearts of many foster children that did not tumble one step further onto judgement in Bentley's heart. He gave her the benefit of wondering to this day by leaving her story open, acknowledging the fact that she did visit, though sporadically and just a handful of times. He extended kindness to this woman and respect for the choice that she made for he was not in her financial circumstances and did not walk her steps in life.

Bentley was separated from his brother at a young age, not knowing where his brother was. He was pulled from one foster home to the next until he landed in the home of a farm family in the rural Midwest. One would presume this is the happily ever after for a foster child, an idyllic place for a boy, but for this particular family, Bentley was taken in simply to be an extra set of hands. One more young man to help run the daily operations of the farm. He was clothed and fed, but the care he received beyond that was as business-like as his role there.

Bentley also supported himself and the family through a job at the local general store. One day while working in the back, a man entered the store. He came asking for Bentley. So, his manager went back and fetched Bentley, "A man is here to see you."

Curious, Bentley approached the counter to greet the gentleman with friendly respect. The fellow said to Bentley bluntly, "I'm your father. I just wanted to see what you looked like." then turned and walked out the door. Bentley never saw him again. He had nothing to say about his father beyond sharing this story. The adages come to mind that *a picture was worth a thousand words* and *since there was nothing nice to say,* Bentley *said nothing more at all.*

In the midst of these years, Bentley felt a pull to go to church. So each Sunday, he set forth on his bike down that country road he now lived on and pedaled himself seven miles to the Catholic church nestled in the nearest town. There, he found the Lord. Perhaps that was the source of the easy-to-laugh jolliness that he carried with him everywhere he went, or his giving spirit like only few men I've ever known. How generous?

There was a term for people who summered up north; those who spent the weeks from Memorial Day to Labor Day in moose country and then ventured to warmer climates to count out the rest of the year's days until they return again. That term is snowbirds. (Marshall calls them sissies. But you'll hear about Marshall in a later chapter.) Bentley is a snowbird up north. When he arrives to his cabin in the spring, there is much nesting to be done to ready his summer home for the memories that lie ahead. Windows to be washed, deck to be sprayed, pontoon to be pulled out of the barn and into the lake, four-wheelers to be readied to drive, cabin to be cleaned and stocked, and lawns in real need of mowing.

Yet what did he do first thing when he arrived, knowing my mother and I resided for the month in the rental cabin across the road? When he pulled into the driveway to enter his garage, he made it his very first task to wheel out his late wife's blue bicycle with its black and white hard seat and green handlebars, air up the tires just so. Even test-driving it to be certain, before delivering it to our little cabin door with a big grin. "I thought you'd like to have your bicycle to ride while you're up here." Moments like those I keep record of in my mind's eye.

Not so long ago, Mom and I were in our rental cabin for our summer trip when a terrible piece of news ran across the screen on the morning news. A hit and run had happened down state. An eighty-eight year old man pulling a trailer was T-boned by an F150, sending him rolling into the ditch four times before landing upside down. The name that followed made us scream in shock and sob in sorrow over what something like that would do to a body that old.

But we underestimated the fighter in our friend. He told us months later, "When I woke up, the visor was shoved up in my neck. My arm was pinned down by the seat belt, so once I got myself out of that! Well, I shucked that thing right out of there and I just started kickin'. I wasn't gonna wait for no ambulance to come 'n' get me. There wasn't anybody on that road. I knew I needed to get out of that car." By the time rescue crews arrived, Bentley had already extracted himself from his small black truck. They life flighted him to the hospital to mend his broken ribs and shoulders and all the things gone wrong. It took him months to recover. But fully he did. By going to the fitness center daily and working himself back into shape. By will.

If you're not already convinced of this man's merit, let me tell you what I see. I see someone who exemplifies the powerful truth that we can choose who we want to be. Bentley came from an upbringing that told him he was not wanted, not loved, discouraged, time and time again. Many kids would grow into adults who live in a place of fear or anger from those repeated disappointments, or self-loathing from those messages of not mattering. But Bentley made a hundred choices that colored his life differently. He chose to not judge. He chose to give grace to his mother. That was the first of many choices that led him down a path of giving and joy. One that dwelled in what he had, not resenting what he did not. He chose to let go of his father's lack of caring. Chose to love the loons. Chose to give like all that's his is ours. And at the age of eighty-eight when his body was crumpled and smashed, crumpled, and crunched, he chose to fight. With a spirit of persistent determination. And he still stands tall at ninety-two today, shoulders shaking with laughter, still tinkering. And through those many little choices that made this man, there's a freedom in every rise and fall of those shoulders when he laughs.

Reflection: The Dance of Trees

In the winter when it snows, there are two ways saplings respond. Some bear the snow, and then, they break. Some, somehow, they bend. With the curvature of an archway that a couple could pass through for marriage or one may bow under unto a cave, that bend all the way to the ground. How does a tree, so fibrous and firm, sturdy and strong, do that? Bow that way? And how, if ever, does it bounce back in the spring when the snow loosens into gentle waters? They do. Each and every one of them do rise again, and let me tell you, they rise taller than they did before. It's those trees that can bend who show the magic of survival within us all. In that magic is the flexibility of true response that is allowing nature to be and yourself to be with it. It's in the formative years that we must allow ourselves the grace of accepting change. Grace unto ourselves and unto the world by bending. Through this simple yet ornate act, we allow those changes to work in every fiber of our being. By the time we're done bending, each season of change has made us stronger on a cellular level in a way no other choice but graceful bending could. Then, my dear reader, artful sapling, is when you know who you really are from a core strong enough to face the wind with arms that reach extravagantly for the sun.

Life: How to Heal a Memory

"You know, I think these could be cancerous. It'd be better if I cut them off to be sure." shared my father.

I was thirteen standing in the procedure room after hours. Fluorescent light cast out into the dark hallway where somewhere across the building, my dad's boss sat in her office typing at her desk. Everything in me did not want to do this. My eyes pleaded no.

"Are you sure? Is that possible?" my mother asked with a blend of fear and question in her eyes.

"I don't think it's possible." I piped up. This was ridiculous, incredulous. Crazy. And I was alarmed at where this was going at a fast rate.

My voice was ignored. "You know," he replied to Mom, "it isn't likely, but with these kinds of moles, you can't be too careful. They could become cancer at any time down the road." He was assuming his all-knowing voice he used with patients. Something about it made people feel like he was looking out for them while at the same time instilled a sense that he held sage wisdom beyond their reach. I wasn't buying.

"Really?" I sounded assertive. I didn't mean to, but I needed to be. My insides churned at the illogical logic he was presenting and my screaming gut instinct that this was wrong. This was not what I wanted.

He turned away from me. From that motion, I knew where my dad's intentions stood. "I'm thirteen. I can't have cancer. I don't want to do this." Mom's eyes were filled with the fear he put there. The fear of a potential danger. Fear born of a father's manipulation of a mother's love, fear I couldn't bear her feeling. I let out my fighting breath. I conceded. Sickness filled me up inside.

He told me to lay down on the exam table, mentioning he was low on numbing serum and it may not last or work. After dubiously injecting me, he began to cut the three places he'd chosen around my neck and at my chest.

I remember lasering in on the grate over the fluorescent light bulbs, the cabinets, the ceiling tile above me. The longer it went on, my bravery faded into a wince. Then a whine. I gripped the edge of the table. The scalpel cut and cut. I couldn't imagine how such small places took so long. Three small incisions around my neck: the front, the side, and the back. My chest was the place that took the most time, just inches from my chin. "Are you almost done?" My words sounded like a choke.

"I'm making sure I get it all." he replied casually. He was critical of my bleeding more than I should. Said blood was in his way, slowed him down. That scared me. I wanted to know what he was doing to my body, what it looked like, what I looked like now. I tried to be brave. But the longer he cut, the more deeply and sharply the pain seared. Tears streamed down my face and I began to cry uncontrollably. He became irritated with me. "We're going to have to stop because you're moving."

"It's hurting so much. When is this going to be over?" I sat up to get away for just a moment. Blood ran down me. My mother caught it with her tissues. I tried to look, but it wasn't in my line of sight. My pain reflected in my mother's eyes. She gently rubbed my ankle, inquiring at my dad's reply. He didn't have one. *What was I allowing?*

I laid back down. The pain felt like a steak knife. It *was* a knife. I *didn't want this* . . . but I respected my Dad. I *wanted to run away* . . . *but I was already too far in, undone. I wanted to stand up for me* . . . but not if it meant my mom being scared. I *wanted it to stop* . . . but at this point, there was nothing I could do. My cries came out from desperation and pain and wanting it to stop. My mind went to the woman in the office. His manager. I wished so much that she could hear me. Wished she would come and stop this. Wished she would understand. No one did. No one did because no one saw past the veneer to understand what was really happening in this moment, or in my world. For that, I felt deeply and entirely alone. I told myself I wasn't being brave. I swallowed my pain and pushed deep. I got quiet.

More than two hours after it began, it was over. From the back seat, I let my emotions run through me. When you save them for later, feelings can come in rapid floods. Over the course of those three blocks home, I felt and thought so many things.

What had I done with my ability to see through him and sense the truth? With my knowledge, I'd chosen to give up the power to save myself a lot of pain. I'd fed manipulated fear and fed his desires. Sparks of betrayal seethed into my skin and settled onto my heart with a smoldering burn. It was a burn I was not familiar with. A fire that wasn't a part of who I was nor the me I wanted to be.

You see, resentment is like a fire. It can consume you in a wild, hungry blaze before you realize that you've lost all sense of who you are. Until the world has lost your light beneath a blinding fire that, in reality, is as dark and irrevocable as ash. I sensed that evidence of its destruction sat before me in the driver's seat from a life that came before us too.

I would not allow this spark to ignite a fire in me.

I was not willing to feed this blaze. I would feed my light instead. So in one swift, iron-clad decision, I swept it away and let the wind that came in from the opening car doors clear my heart. Wiser.

I walked into the house feeling very alone that day. I wanted consolation from no one. Because no one understood. No one saw the depth of the dark but me nor felt it. If it were up to me, no one but me ever would feel that pain. I felt so . . . isolated.

I didn't understand then that I was turning his hate inwards. With the responsibility I'd placed upon myself. With his every word and every act that I took to heart. And now, with every time I gazed at my skin in the mirror. The skin that was red and raised and disfigured and seared with pain. The scarring skin that only seemed to grow.

I didn't want to allow these harmful acts to expound our circumstances with my anger. I just didn't realize that regardless of what you choose to do with them, the feelings you have still exist, and they have to go somewhere. What I was doing was my natural inclination. It was more natural to sacrifice me. I didn't ever want to impose my feelings on others. It was easier for my heart to hate me. Maybe that feeling was even unnoticeable. Like stepping out into the rain already wet.

The emotion that settled in the deepest was a longing sense of loneliness. It was a sensation that I would have for years to come. Alone for seeing. Alone for understanding the depth of things no one else could see. What could I see so clearly beneath the surface when loving required me to dishonor that gift? I didn't realize yet that this clarity was the place from which I was meant to lead my life. And that once I did, I'd never feel alone again. I was abandoning myself, alone in my choices. Always honor your heart and soul's speak. For they hold the keys to never being alone.

Over the coming weeks, the stitches came out. I was relieved to be a step closer to this event being over. I was scared at what it all looked like. I was afraid of how quickly it was changing before my eyes.

Over the coming months, the biggest scar, the one on my chest near my neck, began to hemorrhage and swell. My mother coordinated every attempt she could to make it better. In the three years between ages 12 and 15, I got steroid injections into my scar, silicone sheeting, creams, bandages, but none of that worked. Ultimately, it was decided the only thing left to do was to cut the scar off and see if it wouldn't come back again. After the procedure with the plastic surgeon, I quickly realized it was all recreated, only bigger this time.

My spirit was exhausted by this road. I feared I'd live with these pains that took my breath away forever, that I'd always have this ugly scar below my face. So that no one saw my face. So I was judged. One Sunday morning, I relented on my private resolve. I came to my father. I asked him to look at it. I asked him, "I've tried everything, and it's only worse. Why does it look this way? Why does it hurt so badly each day? I almost can't take it."

Standing at his bedroom door with a casual authority in his voice, he said, "Keloid scarring was likely in this area. I actually thought about that beforehand. I just didn't say anything." *Did he actually mean this?* I felt slapped. Walking back down the empty hallway, my understanding of his intent deepened even further with that hit of horror and an ache felt from a place where love should be.

Then, like I did with so many things between him and I, I blamed myself. *I should know better than to trust him. I should have seen this coming. I should have thought of this .I know better.* And thus, the language of self-abuse compounded my experience, and it carried forth onto all my experiences for years and years to come. I didn't realize I was hurting my heart. I truly thought I was responsible.

Over the years, from age 15 well into my 20's, pain worse than I had the day I'd gotten that last scar seared into my chest. Debilitating pain I have no words for. It took my breath away for long moments, stopped me mid-sentence. As I matured into a woman, the swollen, ugly scar that marred my chest became a conversation piece by the way adults spoke to its mass instead of my eyes, the way children mocked it.

I covered it. I was burdened by the layers of clothing that I thought it took to keep people from knowing it was there, to keep from having to address it. I was sickened by my reflection in the mirror. But clothes touching it made it feel sick. A sick feeling that seeped everywhere. Shame, hurt, remorse, self-blame.

Over a decade after it happened, after a decade spent looking critically at my reflection, a realization dawned on me as I looked tiredly into the bathroom mirror. This scar was a part of me. I'd spent years fighting the existence of this piece of my body. I'd felt sick over it. I'd resented its existence. All of that fighting and loathing, and shame took so much out of me. I was tired. Tired of feeling defeated and defiled in spite of myself.

I took a deep breath. I breathed in my reflection. It was me. I was directing all these feelings towards a piece of myself. And this piece of me wasn't going away. *Do I want to live my whole life feeling this way? Hiding a piece of me, hating and resenting it? Feeling all these things toward my own skin, toward myself? I let my breath out in resolve. No, I did not. I would not.*

And so began my mission. I began to make myself look at my scar longer every time I met the mirror. I didn't allow harsh or wincing eyes. I made myself look at my scar with a different kind of gaze, an accepting gaze *and feel it too.* A gaze that released my shame and invited in grace. A gaze that didn't connect my sense of self with the hurt and regret. A gentler energy. Every time I met the mirror, I forced myself to look at it, to encounter my bad feelings and turn them into good. To understand them in a new way.

Time is a funny thing when coupled with facing yourself in the mirror with your heart. With attention and acceptance, time can heal. I kid you not, that swollen rigid, tender, stabbing-with-pain scar, the one that seared deeply upwards of ten times a day, the one that had undergone every medical procedure known for its kind, slowly, almost imperceptibly, but amazingly perceptibly to me, went away. Its thickness flattened. Its pains subsided. The redness faded away. The tenderness too. And along with its physical transformation came a sincere inner change as well. I was loving my skin, loving my journey, loving myself.

Until one day, I looked into that mirror and as if suddenly, I had a chest that was truly healed, beautiful. My skin was no longer red. My scar, no longer swollen and thick. The steak knife pains had gone away. And so had the knives from my eyes. If you ask me, I will tell you, that scar on my chest, right below my face, healed from the inside out. With forgiveness and grace toward my heart. With Love. Now, when I look at myself in the mirror, I see me, not a flaw. I don't really notice my scar anymore, but when I do look at it, I see a part of me mended by the magic that is acceptance and forgiveness to myself. Love's power within. I wear it as the outward jewelry of my inward healing.

Reflection: Pine Branches

New growth on a pine tree in spring is a lot like people. Starts out small and tender, a pale green that tinges in the heat of day and bends in the storms of night. But as it grows, the elements harden its needles to bear the storms. The very elements that challenge those newborn needles deepen its color so it collects the sun's energy as its own. They strengthen it into something that can withstand and even thrive in the brutal thirty-below winds of the northern winter skies. They prepare what's new and vulnerable for the tests of the Earth, so that, with the life of the tree, each one's beauty only deepens and grows.

There's no deeper dimension to the color green than pine needles shining in the setting sun. I look at them in wonder. That's what God has done for me. Mind, body, and soul.

Life: Together

When you're happy, a funny thing starts to happen. The world begins to fall into place. In our happy place, a new world and a new life were falling in like pieces of a puzzle around us. They all seemed to fit together in a picture that spoke of things I'd never experienced before. Each new friend showing me a beautiful way. Independent as we were, here we lived a life that allowed us to be open. The greatest feeling I remember having for the very first time was being appreciated for all of whom I was and gaining a family and community because of it.

Mom and I had time to share even more in our special bond we had with one another during our stays in that humble abode. We took time for our hobbies and shared our hearts long into the night without ever interruption of our fun and our closeness we shared.

I valued the memories that were sewn into pieces of my mother's heart. Some pieces held hurt that transformed into grace by her own goodness. Other memories were of moments and people who made her feel full, even if their absence from this world left an empty space in their wake. I realize that every memory had pieced together important parts of who she was. Mom shared her memories, each of them important to me because they sewed the fabric of her life I'd never known before and magnificent people in my family who came before me.

She told me of her Grandma H. who would sit in her chair with her legs crossed at the ankle, rubbing her feet now and then, making those patent shoes squeak quietly. "Her skin was always so soft and she smelled so *good.*" Mom would smile through happy, missing tears. "We just couldn't get enough of her, especially the girls. We'd all sit around her and hug her and rub her arms and say, 'I love you grandma.' and she'd make this little noise, like a happy 'hmm.' She was so *sweet.*" She visited her grandma often, going for walks, lunch, over to her house.

She told me of how Grandma H. got "sick headaches," and my grandpa was the only one she would call. There was something about his quiet, gentle, steadfast love that she needed the most in those times. Just like mom and me. *My papa taught my mom what love is, just as my mom has been teaching me,* I thought.

I thought to myself too, *what a beautiful reflection of love.* Grandma H. had a heart that poured out to her children and grandchildren, and they reflected that love immensely back to her.

Her Grandpa W. would pick her up and take her fishing. Just the two of them because her brothers proved they couldn't behave. They'd fuss and fight until all the fish were scared away and their day was gone too. But not Mom. She treasured those days with her grandpa. She still remembers fondly the special snack he'd bring for her to have while he drank his morning coffee. Their quiet visits and trips to the best concessions stand there ever was at the pay-per-catch pond. I was comforted in her memories, feeling as if I knew them too. Knowing that I came from such people meant something to me. It meant I came from love. And to me, that was an important line.

Life: Jack

What grows from being a man like Bentley is having a lot of friends. Everybody knew Bentley and they'd drop in to see him. His joy and generosity was infectious and everyone wanted to bask in it even for a little while. I loved watching the pep go into his step after a nice chat in the driveway with one of the guys.

On one extended stay of a summer, we were met with the frustration of being bumped out of our cabin without notice for a weekend. A promotion that allowed a fleet of runners to fly in and stay to try the space for free.

Naturally, we turned to Bentley, knowing we could lean on him in a time of need. To think how many people likely did that in their day. We rented his place for the weekend. It was nice to be in his space. He wasn't staying there at the time anyway. Mom and I played Katherine's simple yet beautiful piano together, imagining her days at the bench and giggling over duets and fun and simple songs. We watched the sunset over the lake as Bentley had quietly done so many times before. We read a Christmas card still atop the basket at the foot of Katherine's chair granting a peak into her heart which reflected the depth of his. It was a memorable couple of days that seemed fated when at first we'd been so ruffled up.

Fated for the rap on the door we didn't expect and the strange man standing at the other side when we swung the storm door open, we were both caught totally off guard, startled actually. We expected it was Bentley coming by to tinker, but a well-dressed man stood on the porch. And he was nothing but smooth.

"Well hello ladies. I'm Jack Turner. I was wondering if Bentley's here?" He peered around for a moment as if looking for Bentley.

"No actually we're staying here at his house for a couple of days while the marathon passes through."

"Well Bentley said he had a couple of gals staying at his place. I had to come over and check it out." His head cocked back in a chuckle to himself. "You see, I'm staying here with some friends across the street. We like to four wheel and go on the trails and such. We have cocktail hour at five o'clock. You're more than welcome to join us. Absolutely. We would love to chat. Come on over."

Nowadays we live in a world where chivalry can so often be misconstrued. An encounter like this would have been off-putting to many women of the modern era. But Mom and I were not of our era nor were we quick to judge. There was something special that lay beneath the surface of this polished, polite, if overtly smooth, white-haired man with eyes as blue as the Great Lakes. And it was enough to send us walking over to the cabin across the way, half wondering to ourselves what we were getting ourselves into.

When we arrived, we were amazed at the sight of four men who'd prepared a neatly set table with what indeed were cocktail glasses made do out of rental cabin cups on a thoughtfully placed green picnic table. Each sat politely in his seat. The eldest greeted us with a genuine smile. "Well hello ladies."

Carlton and Henry were clams in sealed shells. You could see their minds mulling over what they knew their wives would be thinking when they heard of this "cocktail hour" Jack arranged. Good for them! Couldn't blame them!

Passing on the cocktails, we shared easy conversation and laughs like old friends. Like this arrangement had always been.

That friendship blossomed as we joined them for visits between trail rides, hearing of their glories and escapades of recent times and years gone by. Mostly, they trail rode in the woods with ninety-four-year-old Lawrence ever leading the helm, favoring main trails so he could speed full throttle. It was amazing this man could do all that, exuberant and spry in wit and wisdom too. Let alone a whole group of friends who did the same, all seeming to have captured the same depth in mind and heart. The same capacity to breathe life through investment in each other.

As our friendship grew, they invested in us too. Between summers, a phone call from Jack would light up our day. He'd give us a ring when we least expected just to see what us gals were up to. We'd share pieces of our life and hear about his routines at home with his girlfriend, Arlene, taking her for an evening milkshake, or his visits to shut in neighbors. He was a wonder. Mom and I smiled to each other knowingly each time we heard his classy "Bye-bye" at the end. Though the character makes the man, investment made Jack care to call us now and then like a true friend would; it's the little things too. The little things like that "Bye-bye" that we still remember fondly as an endearing piece of Jack.

When we had a civic issue with the local board, Jack took pen to paper as if it were his own. Our guys rallied on our behalf not just on moral principle but for the care of us and our cabin we'd just settled into. And when we did settle in, we invited our guys to dinner of course. And what did they bring? A housewarming gift.

One year, the guys got stuck staying in some rental cabins a ways down the road. We missed their drop in visits and roaring take offs on the "machines." It just wasn't the same.

A rap came at the door. We peeked out. No car in the drive. Odd. Opening the door, we found Jack's polite smile and beautiful, kind eyes. Carlton's toothy smile stood quietly next to him. "Hello gals. We were wondering if you'd be available for a fish fry at Lawrence and I's cabin tomorrow night."

That was enough to light us up. They didn't want us to bring a thing. Them making dinner was so endearing and sweet. It felt good that they'd missed us too! My mind couldn't help but be a bit amused at the thought of what they might put together. We *were* accepting an invitation to a fish fry at a hunting cabin in the north woods among a group of trail dusted men on a guy's trip, a group accustomed to the tradition of baked bean cookouts and lavish breakfast fries. Mom said, "You haven't seen Jack cook. He can cook a nice meal." This I had to see.

When we stepped into their warm abode on the crisp night of the June evening, we found a dining table neatly set center stage. Each gentleman sat freshly clean and nicely dressed for dinner after their day out. I felt humbled as they made sure we had a seat and a drink. Lawrence tapped his fingers nervously on the table, one of those little things about him. He made casual conversation in his lilting voice that was like no other. I watched in amazement as a domestic side of Jack revealed itself to my wide eyes. Donning potholders to peek in the broiler of the apartment-sized stove, he checked his baking whitefish filets and accompanying cheesy potatoes. I'm glad mom and I can talk with our eyes because we both saw that scene unfold, and I think only our eyes had words for it. There was an amusedly gentle I *told you* so somewhere in our ocular conversation.

It's fun being pleasantly surprised, seeing new layers of people you thought you knew. The evening was thoroughly enjoyable, sharing stories, local news, and a common sense about life that true friends naturally find together.

Henry was a fascinating person to talk to, every word thoughtfully chosen with a good measure of wit. Yet he held back to let Jack take the lead, or Lawrence when he spoke. There was a sort of respect of age that went without saying. And Carlton, he just stayed quiet. We weren't sure what he thought at times. He seemed comfortable around us, just shy. His eyes said he was a man who wasn't quiet for lack of caring but instead took everything in. The stories shared told much about each man.

Jack told us of his childhood growing up on a farm. A genuine rodeo cowboy from the Wild West drifted into town each summer for work. He'd long ago hung his hat, having been thrown from the bull many a time. He was broken and pieced back together with the surgical ingenuities of the 1920s that likely brought him a good deal of pain. The circus brought him steady employment through most of the year. All except for summer. After walking across the country each year to a humble family farm near the Great Lakes, he rested in their barn each night and forked hay, calved, herded, and cared for the farm by day. A better ranch-hand could not be had. But what stuck out to little Jack, when he ventured into the barn to visit his cowboy, was the cowboy's answer to a question his father asked the man weekly.

"Anything you'd like me to pick up for you from town?"

"A bag of M&M's." was his weekly reply. No more, no less.

Each time little Jack came into the stable to visit the cowboy on an afternoon after school, those M&Ms waited just for him. Even retelling it to us, I could see in Jack's face he was just as touched by that small gesture today as he was all those decades ago, maybe more now that he was old enough to value the little things. "He didn't have much. He only walked into the farm with the clothes on his back. But he always asked for those M&Ms to share with me." This long-ago memory kept in Jack's heart goes to show that simple acts of kindness stick with a person all the years of their life.

Marveling too at how a man could endure all his surgeries, be pieced back together, and persist. It was clear to me and to Jack that this man was led by the heart. It's what drove him across the country to the Turner Farm each summer, what motivated his thoughts and desires, and likely what got him through when times got tough. I have to wonder if that's what being a true cowboy really means. If there ever was one, Jack's cowboy sure was it. And what else that man proved was that Jack's heart was as large to serve as his eyes showed because that's the lens through which he remembered his cowboy. It's the lens through which Jack saw the world when it came down to it.

Life: Sudden Change

Then, there was the summer everything changed. The guys came up like clockwork, just like most other things they did on their annual trips. By now, we knew their schedules and they knew ours. With the resonance between us all, they and their equally yoked wives had become loved members of the home that was growing in our hearts. When they pulled in, they'd unload their trailers and come right over to say hello and visit. Dinners and afternoon adventures were yet to come.

One day after arriving for this particular trip, Henry knocked on our door. Jack was leaving. We were friends, and he wanted us to know why. Henry knew Jack would want us to know. He recounted a couple days after arriving, Jack was chatting in the cabin when he suddenly fell from his chair to the floor. They rushed to the nearest ER, a forty-minute drive, and waited word for hours after many tests.

Jack'd had a persistent cough ever since a trip abroad he'd taken to Italy. His doctors downstate thought it was a persistent bug. In fact, the body was saying something was terribly wrong. With this fall, they learned that wrong was something serious that had spread to the brain. Understandably, Jack wanted to go home.

It was all Henry could do to hold in tears that threatened to run down his face as he sat in our living room recounting what he couldn't believe. We all felt the painful void suddenly, inevitably looming between the lines. But in Henry's eyes, there was a lost feeling that said, How could this be, I don't want to let go. It all played across his face in our filled silence as the shock and sadness settled in my own chest. Not a man for expression, unless you were really looking close, the honest pain in Henry's eyes showed just how very deep his well of love for Jack was.

Life has shown me that loving and hurting come in equal measure. And even though some loves come with an inevitable pain, I know it to be overwhelmingly worth the reward and, at times, the responsibility. The silence that weighed between us carried all of this, but for right now, we were going to be Jack's friends seeing him off for his drive home.

I ran over to give Jack one last hug, and I asked the guys if I could take a group photo of the four of them together. It was a beautiful image. In the June sunshine, their smiles captured four men of magnificent character and authentic personality with thousands of trails of memories etched between each other's lives.

Life: Goodbye Jack

The doctor had given Jack six months to live. We kept up with him, and he with us, just as we'd always done. But after six weeks had passed, we received a call. His prognosis had taken a final turn. Mom and I took one look at each other after hanging up the phone, and we packed a bag. It was a six-hour drive to Williamston. We used that time to first call Cecilia. "You're welcome to stay with us." Under the circumstances, we were comforted by her kindness and their opening their home to us. What a special memory that came to be.

Cecilia was a woman so full of zeal for life and a comfort in being herself unmatched by anyone I know. The kind that made her pop her head out the doorway in her shower cap when we arrived for a morning chat. Or had a sparkle in her eye over her own sass. She took delight in life itself, but also in herself in the most tasteful of ways. I loved Cecilia. Their home was comforting, and the way she made it for us was a memory for my own heart.

When we got into Williamston, we took everything in. This was the hometown of Bentley's youth, where Jack built his thirty-five-year-long career, where Henry and Cecilia met at the roller skating rink and Maria and Carlton had their first date at the Sadie Hawkins dance, where they built their careers and became such close friends. The home of their memories was special to us. We pulled up to the address, expecting a respectfully brief visit, knowing this was a time for family and close friends. When we crossed the street, Jack's daughter, Laura stepped out into the road. "Can I help you ladies? Are you here to see Dad?"

"We're friends of Jack's and the guys from up north. We came because we . . ."

"No! . . . NO! You have GOT to be kidding! No! You're the ladies from the north that quilt and embroider?? Ohhh, *that's dad!* Oh my, that's dad. See he let us believe all this time that you were two little old ladies tucked up there in the woods. And I was like, 'Oh Dad, that's nice you're friends to them. That's nice. He had *us* fooled!' This is so like him. See, I needed that today." She pointed up. "Thank you. And you two came all the way down here by yourselves? That is so nice! He is going to love that. Come on in and see Dad."

Mom and I were having one of those conversations with our eyes again, only for a brief moment did we exchange a *Wow*, amusedly loving this moment and the lively daughter kindly welcoming us in.

"We don't want to take time away from family. We just wanted to come to say goodbye to Jack and let him know how much he means to us. How much we care." Mom spoke up as Laura ushered us up the walk.

"You ladies stay as long as you'd like! Have you had dinner yet? My brother Dave here is grilling out." She opened the door, and when we stepped inside, it seemed we were entering on the sacred grounds of a family's bedside vigil. But unlike one I'd ever been witness to. There were eyes full of sadness at moments, but most of all, there was family. Support. Stories. Most of all, love. It was everything you could want in your final hours for yourself and your loved ones. It felt good to know Jack had that in his family. I had an idea of where that love came from. Laura must have noticed we felt suddenly out of place. She swept us right up by his bedside, one on either arm.

"He hasn't opened his eyes for us yet today, and he's not talking anymore, but maybe he'll open his eyes for you two. I bet he will. Just get in real close to him." She stepped back to the foot of his bed.

Mom and I each took his hand and gave them a gentle squeeze.

"Hello Jack." I was suddenly lost for poignant words at the sight of our friend. The shell of this kind soul had changed very much since we'd last talked to him.

"Jack, it's June and Allie from up north. We drove down to see you today. We love you Jack."

"We love you very much, and we wanted to see you. You're so special to us." I added. And as we were speaking his eyelids were moving in a way that looked like he was fighting with all his might to come back from some other world. Coming up from somewhere deep to break through until suddenly and incandescently his crystal sky blue eyes burst open and his whole face lit up into a big smile. His body leaned up out of bed and into that smile in one great act of joy. Us three women marveled and reveled in that joy with him. Mom and I talked and talked with Jack until we knew he needed rest.

Afterward, Laura ushered us onto Jack's terrace. "He's been unresponsive for the past couple of days." She explained the comings of the relatives which cascaded into family stories until we were there much longer than we thought polite. What we were experiencing was an act of candor and kinship. It touched me in a way I won't forget. Our gesture meant as much to Jack's children as it did to their dad, and in that moment, they loved us just the same as he did. An extension of love sent out in familial directions sparked by the magic of true friendship. That evening, it was healing to us all.

Days later, Laura called to tell us her father had passed, surrounded by family. "I want to thank you. You gave my dad one last smile."

He had a funeral different than any other. Just as Jack planned it, his sendoff wasn't one of sadness. The day was a celebration of the family and friendships he built through the years. A hay rack ride filled with his family pulled by nothing less than a John Deere tractor. According to the article in the local paper that Cecilia shared later with us, over a thousand people turned out to remember "one of Williamston's favorites." Likely, they came to remember a thousand small acts of kindness he'd placed in hearts of their own.

Jack had a special sense about people. He knew how to choose a man of depth, call him a friend, bring him into his circle, and make it last a lifetime. He walked into people's lives and showed them steadfast love. And that love was returned tenfold. It presented itself in guys' trips that spanned decades of tradition and bonds of regard and concern that deepened with every passing year. People often wonder what legacy is left in their midst. When Jack knocked on

Bentley's screen door one sunny afternoon in June, true friendship was the powerful legacy he was about to leave in ours and the lasting act of kindness.

Reflection: Legend

There's a Native American legend in honor of the Petoskey Stone. It's a stone that appears to have hundreds of sunshines in it for the fossilization of ancient coral in the Great Lakes. Long ago, people spoke of its magic. They said those sunny imprints symbolized that the sun would ever rise again for another day in the places you love most with those whom you love the most. It's a beautiful legend I keep near. Yet I also see something more in this stone. The Petoskey Stone lies on a beach, gray like any other rock, until the water touches it, revealing the ancient coral imprint of a shining sun. To me, it's like a symbol that, sometimes, it takes the washing of the waves or the rain in life to display the greatest beauty of one's nature.

Life: **Coming Back**

We knew better than to share how special our trips up north were when we got back. He'd want to take them away if we did.

Dad was well taken care of when we were away. Mom made him a home cooked meal for every lunch and dinner we were away and froze it with a label saying what was in each one. She had his laundry laid out just right. Acts of love didn't go undone in her world. Not for anyone, returned or not. It was just the way of her greatly giving heart. I wondered if I could be so generous if I were her. If she didn't do those things, I'm sure our trips would soon have expired. It wasn't us he missed.

We knew how things were at home. It's how it'd always been. But in a bigger way, our life in farm country became more clear after being away. The town looked run down. Our home in the Cornbelt felt even more abrasive than we remembered. It was an adjustment getting back to bracing.

As the gift of a healthy home grew up north, I began to feel like my life was wasted when I wasn't there. These years in my childhood home felt more and more in captivity. I begged and bargained with Mom over plans to leave him with renewed passion. She was a more committed woman than I. She stood by the vows she'd taken and the right thing to do. Honor and love, no matter what. I hated it and I respected it. So, I silenced and lived on.

Sometimes, we have to face the pains inside us before we can move beyond them. Some of us are charged with transmuting those pains for the light we have within, for the light within us all. In our hearts, roots were being planted. Branches were being pruned. I was shifting inside. This was only God's beginning of something beautiful.

Reflection: Connection

Our souls, our spirits, are connected to all things living on the Earth. That's why we feel a peace, an energy within when it rains, through the gentle thunder of the darkened sky and rolling clouds above. Those energies pass through us just as the energy of home passed through me as I entered these woods. It was a perfect rainy day today. Taking in the gentle rain and thunder rolling in over the lake throughout the day was calming and energizing at once. I was alive, within. I was Loved.

Life: The Impacts We Make on Our Selves

My father seemed to resent my very being for a very long time. The competition always remained, but his hatred for me, the spite, took a decade to settle down. It settled because I'd learned how to make peace with him. Stroking his ego, relating to his pessimistic ideas; it went against my nature to be ingenuine, to submit the will of my heart. It hurt to give up those parts of me, but I found those sacrifices worth the peace that they brought to our home.

But was all that acceptance and peace worth the submission of boundaries and worth that I was teaching my heart? I was training myself to submit my will and say my boundaries don't matter. Was tolerance and placation the right thing? Was it worth teaching myself to love the unattainable? To reach for the unreachable?

We all meet heart-altering crossroads in our lives. Death, betrayal, loss, abuse. It's how we respond to these challenges inside our hearts that determines the quality of the rest of our lives. Determines the cycles we perpetuate or break. Determines what we teach our children. His heart may not have been whole, but he taught mine with those choices. I felt, *He didn't want my love. My love didn't matter. He didn't express love because he didn't love me. Maybe this time? No, he didn't love me. Maybe if I'm more? He didn't love me . . . I didn't love me. Something must be wrong with me.* I felt, *This kind of disrespect is something that must be held somehow, accepted.* He was making choices in relationships with self and others that were unconsciously shaping mine until, years later, many trials later, I recognized it.

It's a human hope for a child that a parent love and want them. But the truth is that more often than many of us admit and share, we don't all have our parents' hearts.

In attempt to heal that, some people spend their entire lifetimes chasing their parent's love in other forms. Be it clothed in a spouse or friend. Finding people who are like that undesiring parent fills an inner gap. As if that person grants us a means to resolve the unrequited desire. But it never seems to work; it always has the same outcome, one where we're left feeling worthless and tired, maybe even empty. Until finally, after many depleting attempts, we find within ourselves, for ourselves, the acceptance and love we hunger for. By accepting we deserve love, we're worth love, we are love, we release need altogether. That is the time when we feel full. That is when life begins anew in that we are free. First, of course by experiences, my heart learned.

Life: God Seeks Us Too

I believe there are many paths to faith. Each one is a unique reflection of how God can reach every heart that is willing to open up to Him; to listen, to trust, to believe. My path to God was like that. I'd come to a point in my life when I was uncertainly certain. I knew where my life was headed. It seemed on a natural and hard-earned path. Yet something inside was calling me to listen more deeply within my heart. God was *calling me to Him; calling me to pray.* God was moving my spirit. With His hand reaching out for me to take, God invited me to open my heart to Him more fully, to lean into Him and open my mind to a different path. One that made room for *life* within me. For more love. Every night, when I was alone, I began to pray. It felt so peaceful spending time one-on-one with God. I could feel Him move me, counsel me. And I sought Him.

In that leading, I began going to my cousin's church by an unshakable calling from my spirit. When I followed that calling, I met a soul sister in her and a model of faith. As my faith deepened, I came to revere that intimate relationship between God and me. I understood that awe-inspired, safe, majestic feeling I always got in nature. There, I was in His presence, and I heard Him in my heart.

God helped me to trust my heart, to not feel alone, to manifest the life I wanted and needed, with His assuring hand in mine. The first step was to leave my boyfriend.

Life: Love Learned

I'd learned how much my heart needed to grow when I finally began to explore romantic love. I had patterns ingrained in me I'd yet to discover and uproot. Deep subconscious urges to rectify my relations that manifested in abuse, in fixing, in all the things I'd felt I needed to achieve. What I didn't see yet, what I had wrong, was that we can't heal ourselves by encountering the same turmoils in different forms. We must be aware of them, and then we must face them and release them within ourselves. We must make a different choice.

After the end of the first romantic relationship in my life, a new void was left that little could fill. So easily I felt myself slipping into a sadness that swallowed me up and drained away my liveliness, my inner joy that once defined me. I had loved this one person so unconditionally only to be faced with the most challenging decision of my life; to go. One that nearly broke me but yet made me just the same.

I couldn't help but replay everything over and over in my mind. How could I allow myself to let things go on so long being treated the way I was? How could I be so wrong? How could I have ignored my intuition so many times? I worked to give up the hope I knew was lost; my undying faith that he'd ever become that man I believed was in him if I had stayed the course. It's hard to tell yourself not to have faith in someone you love. But, it's harder to live with placing your love and your faith in a relationship where true love cannot be shared.

I woke up in bed from a nightmare. In it, I'd agreed to meet him somewhere. As I approached him, I immediately knew my decision was ill advised. He was charming, as always, yet I could feel his calculated nature just beneath the surface. It sent a stillness through my bones. He somehow got me in the car with him and as conversation carried us out onto the highway, I realized we were picking up to an alarming speed, a speed that reflected his heightening emotions as the conversation turned. He was trying to get me to return to him.

Though he had a hold on me, I was a strong woman. That challenge he never liked.

I challenged him then, explaining to him why I left and stayed away, reminding him of his words and his actions for which he had no remorse or culpability. Holding him accountable always flared his temper, and it did in this moment through the pressing of the gas pedal. As his anger rose, so did the speedometer. He took an exit off the highway that curled around a cliff, and I suddenly knew. My heart dropped out of my stomach. His words boiled down to one message: *If I can't have you, nobody can, and I won't be here either.* As he curved around, to my surprise, he slowed the car rather than flying over the edge. The second it was safe, I burst out of the car. But he was there, ranting and coming toward me. I could tell he was making his decision. Nobody knew where we were now. Even if I did run, there was nowhere for me to go. Could I overpower him? From experience I knew the answer but my spirit said otherwise. I felt like a snake teaser trying to keep him at bay. But always at this point, the dream would end. Never revealing the fate of this situation, which quite deftly illuminated the tenor of the relationship and its reverberating fears. Sometimes, when I had the dream, he would drive the car off the cliff, but as with most falling dreams, I'd awaken before impact. I didn't like how my subconscious reminded me of feelings I wanted to forget. I wondered if I'd always look over my shoulder, ever moving the hidden key at the house.

There came a point when thoughts of him were something I knew I didn't want to have anymore. I chose to fill my void by living my life more fully. I sat down and made a list. It was a list comprised of things that I wanted to do, accomplish, work toward, and people who I knew lifted me up that I wanted to remain connected to and had become separated from. I vigorously chased those endeavors day by day, keeping my list on the top of my desk at home until I didn't have to look there and force myself in order to follow it. I was building myself back together, more willfully than before.

I went to dinner with friends, even a trivia night. I learned to line-dance, becoming the most spirited on the floor. I faced my fear of water and went jet skiing and water rafting. I won second place in a 12K and tried my knack at meditation. I danced with a stranger. I went on two dates in one day and kissed them too. I got baptized in my favorite place in the world.

I returned to the living and returned to myself. Somewhere along the way, it dawned on me that I was strong. Not simply for having learned to honor my heart, but for respecting myself enough to stand up for it, to have a voice for it without the accompanying guilt of how I'd impose. I was building a healthier relationship with myself. I was beginning to learn how to love myself.

In time, and in finding me again, I found that I was capable of loving someone unconditionally and letting them go. From here forward, I could use my mind and my heart in choosing a man, a friend, a place, but my spirit would have the final say. If he didn't kill my body, he surely would have killed my spirit, if I didn't go and stay away. It wasn't until years later that I'd make the connection from this man to my father. In the finely calculated language, the air of discrete threat, brooding need. My first boyfriend was the same kind of man clothed in younger skin. I feared that I was drawn to him. The old adage that they say about daughters and fathers had come true, but what they failed to add is that some daughters blindly enter those relationships to learnedly break the cycle.

Reflection: Polarities Defined

If you live with the gift of being an empath like I do, please be aware of your relations. There's a certain type who reflects your light with an equivocal dark, the narcissist. Both are needed in this world, yet the dynamic is one to be weary of.

I believe narcissists are capable of love. When the first note of infatuation strikes, when they sizzle with the observance of another worthy of their pride, they're feeling. They're getting what they desire most: emotion, feeling. The things they have a hollowing need for the most because they've so long ago turned away from them. When you're an empath, like me, you give that to them, and they do feel because of you. You make them feel like a drug, like all they've wanted for a very long time. That's why for us as empaths, the experience mirrors this notion.

Because for us when the first note of infatuation strikes, when they sizzle with the observance of another worthy of their pride, there is nothing else in higher affection and grace. It's like a high you go on. A spell-like love cast just for you. For narcissists are as intuitive as you. They know what you think, you need, you feel. And as if by command, you feed it to them while they quietly observe, tuning into your heart. Until you're lost without them.

They need you for your intuitive dose of feelings just as much as you need them for their intuitive dose of reassurance. But it's a toxic interdependency prescribed to fall apart. Because narcissists have made the choice long ago to not feel their feelings. And after some time, the rush of yours will no longer fill their hollow places, left vacant from that choice, the high they so desire. When you're not the drug you used to be, they'll want more. They'll look further, they'll abuse, they'll discard. No longer will you feel the intuited reassurance you had before. They don't have the feelings to desire you anymore without the ability to connect. It's the result of the choice they made long ago not to feel. It's confusing for you because you feel so much. You try and you reach. You convince yourself to ignore the signs, but the solemn truth is the reality that stares you in the heart. You know it because your eyes see through the soul.

In these relationships, neither is really a victim or a predator. You're just two people in need. Two people who find a space in their hearts that needs filled. Drawn by the natural balance of polarity. Some empaths are drawn to narcissists as a reprieve from their own feelings. Some believe connection is an ability inherent by belief alone. Narcissist to empath attraction is a call for knowing thy heart and soul better than that of any other.

If you've been where I was . . . Why did you need reassurance? Why did you take treatment that you otherwise would never have tolerated? Why did you undefine boundaries in the name of what really was a lack of love? Why were you drawn to this within? Because at the bottom, you don't believe love will last? You don't believe someone will truly love you for all that you are? Because you are afraid of being unloved? You're beautiful in full form. But you haven't always been loved because others haven't been able within themselves. Perhaps you haven't loved you that way either . . . Don't accept that as belief of yourself. You are wanted. You are loveable. You are so loved. You deserve every happiness in the world. It is coming for you. It has already happened in your plan. Everything within you that has been broken down is rebuilding as you touch it with love for yourself, acknowledge it with grace. You are cherished, by you, by me, by God, by the one who will come along and take you in his arms to stay. Yes, he's there, the path is direct. Believe. Believe in love. Choosing to believe makes the impossible quite possible, beautiful, and most of all makes it happen.

Life: **Run and Admittance**

But I attracted these men again and again. Life became a box of repeated disappointed hopes I couldn't escape from. It became a glass box from which I could *feel* each of them yet all they could do was *see* me, and the surface was the last place I wanted to be.

It was hard for me to admit I needed help. Hard to admit dependence. Hard to say that I had pain inside because then I would feel weak and broken. But truly, for a person to admit what they've been through and recognize how it had affected them mentally, spiritually, and emotionally takes far greater fortitude than the stoicism of ignoring the presence of such natural human challenges. These very deep seeds are the sprouts to our soul's growth. With God. If only we choose to water them and help them grow into strengths, gifts within ourselves to help others.

I was halfway through an early run as orange and pink streaked magnificently across the dark morning sky. It was a day my heart felt heavy with home. My feet beat emotion through me and into the pavement in release. I didn't want to feel this anymore. I knew I carried so much weight in my heart. Even worse, I knew it transgressed into my relationships spelling a lifetime of entrapment in a cycle I knew I must break. I must get out of this chokehold of sickness I feel towards myself. Self-critical loathing over seemingly nothing at all. Tears streamed down my face. *God, I want to release this pain I feel with my father. Please help me release my hurts. Help me move past it all so that it has no effects on my life anymore. I can't do this without you. I am not strong enough without your help and guiding hand, but I will listen. I want to follow. Please help me. I need you. Please. I can't live feeling like this anymore.* My prayer felt like a promise, and from that day forward, things began to change. But as it is said, chaos precedes new life.

Reflection: Song of Silence

I set forth on my board. The intimacy of being alone with nature made all of my senses relax into reverie as I cast out upon the lake. Where would I go today? I already had an idea. My gut churned, drawing me toward something different. Uncharted territory where I could find a new part of myself, of life. For isn't that a point of it all? As it is said, "I lose myself and find my soul."

Waves sparkled with a reflection of periwinkle blue and a deep shade dark as night. As the water grew deeper, navigating became a challenge of both mind and spirit, even emotion. These parts of me worked in cohesion to get where I wanted to go as the waves churned under and around my board in conflicting directions with the shifting winds. I felt a symbolism in it.

We have to desire the challenge of meeting our very own depths. Riding the course of our inner turmoils to better understand the churning, richly colored dimensions of our inner selves, of life. Inside, we find a force of nature so much like these waters.

To meet each wave of life and respond to it requires a blending of the mind to focus, the body to steer your course, and the spirit to discern the elements at play. The water and the wind may churn without ceasing, with torrents of rain across your way. Those are exactly the moments when you channel your depth. It's your focus, your drive, your rhythmic breath in saving response to your emotions that steadies you. This channeling of feeling and fortitude is your energy expelled into the world around. You're a force to be reckoned with. When you harness yourself in this way; mind, body, and soul in unison, you can handle the deep that is you, that's life. Accomplish the deep. Achieve the deep. When you do, we will finally be.

You have, after all a depth that's richly, intimately your own. Behold your depth with the sincere power of your heart and soul.

Life: Investigative Discovery

The angst I felt came this time every summer. Summer's end. Knowing that my mother's and my time together in our favorite place in the world was down to its final days made my insides ache. To ease the pain, I stepped outside into the coming evening. The wind was coming in off the lake. It was strong, and I could smell the water as if I were seated on the dock already. I knew where I was headed. It wasn't far. I knew I couldn't venture too long or else Mom would worry in these deep north woods. Where I was headed was a simple place that somehow my spirit felt called to. Perhaps for its beauty; the magical way the light of the sunset shined through the branches of the aged poplar and spruce trees. Or perhaps for the knowing my spirit seems to have about the life-altering things that will come its way.

Nevertheless, I approached the small fisherman's easement, with a longing that I couldn't deny. I went for it. Looked left and right. No one was watching, so I stepped into the empty lot that adjoined the easement. It had been wooded and grassy for as long as I'd been coming here. Totally uninhabited land, small as the parcel may be.

Though I was sort of in a neighborhood, I felt this strange sensation of stepping into the woods on this lot for how thick the trees were. The privacy gave me all the more courage to do some sleuthing. See what I could see. Trees, ferns, weeds, tall grasses smashed by last season's snow, and wait. The corner of a faded orange sign. Perhaps it used to be red. The elements of nature up here were not gentle to the objects of mankind. My heart leapt when I saw it.

I quickly dropped to the ground and pulled and pulled at the layers of grass and plants that covered it. Many seasons had passed since this sign had proudly stood in the ground, but for whatever reason it was buried now; it might as well have been buried treasure to me! I was going to call that phone number and find out. I committed the numbers to memory over and over again and ran as fast as my legs would carry me to Mom. My romantic trip down the easement at sunset postponed for a later date.

"Well you DO realize that is the best piece of frontage on the entire lake. My price would be firm." the owner's gruff voice finally conceded after sharing the history of how he'd acquired the land. "I'll have to see if my kids want it first. Give me two weeks, and I'll get back to you."

And so our dream was on a hinge. Was his statement a polite blow off or was he spending two weeks heavily weighing his options with himself and his family in mind? And with his inflated idea of his prime frontage filled with lake muck, carpenter ants, and aged trees, would he return with a prime country club price tag? One we couldn't take on? Well he did take just about his two full weeks to call us back, but when he did, he was purely decisive. He was ready to sell, and his price was firm. It was just beyond our reach, but close enough to stretch for it. Like most any dream. Now was our time to choose.

Dreams are only dreams until we choose to realize them. Life bestows upon us many roads to travel upon and the tools to employ to make those roads into a beautiful journey. The turning point is whether we have the courage and discernment to take those tools in our hands and use them to place those roads firmly under our feet. When I stepped out of our rental cabin that crisp late summer morning, little did I know that I was taking the first step into placing the greatest journey of my life under mine. When Mom and I said yes to our dream, little did we know how far it would take us in the years to come. What saying yes to your dreams can do.

Life: Intro to Church

I'd been going to church for some time. Dinners with my cousin had become a bi-weekly affair. Life felt good. But in getting my groove back, I forgot my best practices. I always held the things dearest to me close to my chest so that they wouldn't be exploited, so I wouldn't be understood too much, so the tools were never in my dad's hands to play inside my heart, my mind.

He noticed my habits. I'd become lax and let him see. When he began asking questions–*Where is this coming from?* and *You must be liking that*–at first, my guard was up. But as time went on, I noticed him reading historical texts on Christianity. He began boasting his knowledge of Jesus and historical fact. I listened, wondering. *Is God working here?* Dad challenged my interest as if my faith did not make sense. Almost daily, he pushed and prodded. I wasn't sure what I was watching unfold, but it gave me a dawning hope. And, against my usual protection, I opened up to him out of that little-girl hope he could *feel*, could *heal*. I took every conversation as a careful opportunity to share Him.

I could see that my father felt upstaged by my faith, but he felt threatened by anything he perceived as my being better than him. By some inner need, he unceasingly felt he must find a way to beat me, whatever it was I did. This churchgoing side of me triggered that. He could not be bested. But in his rivalry, I saw a backdoor open to his heart, through God. If I wasn't able to heal my father, surely God could show him love. After so many years of broken-down faith in changing his heart, I had hope with him again. Whether it were a sincere motivation to pursue God or not, he was. And for that, he was pursuing Love...Could that heal him? Our family? It was worth the risk of opening up to him, quietly, carefully, lovingly, to find if that's a way. I thought so.

He began reading voraciously on Christ and of the Bible. He then tore out the sections of the Bible. When I asked, he sneered and said he didn't like those parts and didn't agree with them. That they weren't accurate or true, so he wasn't going to read them. His stance was, "You know, there aren't any real Christians in most churches. They're there to promote their business, themselves. They all have their reasons. It's disgusting really." But I was watching the turmoil of a shift happening in him of some measure. And I wanted to support it.

Reflection: The Fox

I awakened from a dream, remembering it as if my soul recalled . . .

The fierce wind tousled my silky red coat. One would think I'd catch a chill, but with my dense, soft underlayer I didn't notice a thing. My eyes were fixed on my mate. That same wind threw the waves higher and harder than ever before, nearly to where I could not see him. But he stood tall beyond our lake, transfixed, gazing back at me, in a way I'd never seen before. And something in his air cast a different kind of wave through the powerful, tree-swept wind, a wave of worry that washed right through to the center of me. There was something different in his look. I could feel it. Was something wrong? I wanted to leap forward; make sure he was alright. But my feet wouldn't let me. They were firmly planted on the ground reminding me that I had ten sets of softly pointed ears to watch after, depending on me. I must stay.

So I sat. And wondered. Feeling confused and alone when he disappeared. One would think that he was washed away in the mighty waves, I wondered that. But somewhere inside I knew. Somewhere inside I saw him. Ducking. Running through the ferns. Away. Away from me. Away from our family. Away from our home. Away from his role as a father, as a mate. His back away from my shoulders inside our den each night. I couldn't help but wonder what might have happened if I'd chased after him. But I knew I must stay.

A fox isn't bitter, she doesn't resent. She doesn't cry out in pity or shame. Those feelings are incomprehensible to the innocence of a dear-hearted fox. Rather, I felt overcome with the child-like wonder of being hurt for the very first time. Not grasping that one could unlove another. *Why did he do that?* was all I could say. Most of all, more than anything, I felt alone.

My kits were my love. Besides the forest, of course. I was their caretaker now. It was up to little, young me. And for those seasons, they were my company, my greatest responsibility. I watched over them as well as two parents should. Fed them, safeguarded their home, kept them warm through the night, and when the big tan cat came with glowing golden eyes, eyes that gleamed so intently they spun, I pulled them in tight and I kept her away. I was a good mother, doing it all on my own.

I remembered my life before. For all my days after that fateful moment, more than anything I felt . . . alone. It confused me all the rest of my born days. I couldn't conceive why he would leave, simply didn't understand walking away. I wasn't lonely, I simply felt alone. Alone with my forest. Alone in rearing my kits each season. Alone in life.

There's a certain independence that comes from being alone, the kind that breeds self-sufficiency and knowing the ways and lays of your land, hard earned and connected. My spirit grew strong but stayed tender and true.

Then one day. On a day when the when blew fiercely. The bare trees bent and the dry grass whipped, my hair was tousled yet again. This time coarsened a little by life, faded from age. I laid in a bed of grass in a familiar field, curled up in my tail, alone. I wasn't cold, I had my coat. But I was tired, and my heart was too, for it gave out and laid me to rest. As the wind blew my spirit free to the wind.

Life: **Building on Love**

"How about we place it here, where the grain in the v-groove looks like an extension of the branch." I said, completing the thought that had just entered my mother's mind too. Her eyes smiled as she held the other side of our clock and I hammered in the hole. We knew well that joy was all in the details, and we appreciated every one. This particular detail of our placing the owl-shaped clock on that "branch" was something our guests may never notice when they visited our humble abode, but we would find happiness in for years to come. It became the focal point of our homey living room. That woodsy owl balanced our theme of blended classy-and-cabin. In years to come, he would show us the passing of time up there when hours passed like minutes, and weeks somehow felt like a day.

Together we'd designed it, just the two of us. We'd known how we'd create it for years, and all those years of planning and yearning had made the efforts over floor plans and fixtures seamless. We were a well-oiled interior decorating team. Then again, we worked well at anything we did. We were best friends. No one knew our hearts and minds better than each other. Better yet, no one had cared for them so tenderly. Our bond was something outsiders admired and thought was special. It made me feel good when people recognized that because it *was* special. As special as mother and daughter can be.

In the beginning, our trips up north allowed us to enjoy one another fully. Live fully. Be us fully. We took great joy in every little thing. We worked supportively and efficiently through laying our two thousand pounds of river rock. We collaborated over building our small fence. We kept each other company over the many hours of watering grass seed with the black fly bites to show for our work. We even laughed through cleaning the lake muck together that washed up from the opposite shore. Boy did that stuff stink! There were late nights of looking up at the stars, as abundant as you could ever imagine, sharing in the wonder of the moon. Encouraging her onto sunny bike rides as she gained the courage to test her new knee. Rainy days when all we did was make tapioca pudding and fix each other's hair and plan a movie only to get lost in conversation till all we could see was the outline of each other's silhouettes in the dark. At times, our chats were light and filled with laughter. Other talks lifted weights from the burdens our hearts carried up north from home. In those candid times together, we shared tears of laughter, tears of release, of untold pains and understood ones too.

"How do you spend so much time together and not get sick of each other?" people would ask. They just didn't understand. I couldn't blame them. Most didn't have it this good. Didn't have a mom who loved them as unselfishly with all their heart and soul; who under-stood them and respected them and loved them as a child and a friend. I was lucky, I was blessed, and I treasured every bit of her.

Life: Intentions

My father had been going to a variety of churches around town. Each one he felt was flawed, coming home perturbed at how something was done or a lack of his clients there. Often, he'd make a flippant statement about what he was going to do with his day instead of going to church. But when he saw me going steadily, he remarked on that, his jaw set, his back thrown straight.

He finally decided on the church that suited him most. "I'm going to this one because it has the most clients. They think a lot of me. So, I'm going to go there. The other church has a better service, but I'm going to go where my clients are, at this one."

I wasn't encouraged by his intentions. In that statement, I heard a person equally determined yet misaligned with the true nature of seeking God. He was going to church, but more deeply, he was seeking love and approval from outside sources by means of manipulation and deceit. That was a tricky trap he'd laid for himself because by manipulating everyone, he could feel nothing but inferior and alone. Because he wasn't sincerely himself, he couldn't feel loved for who he was.

When one lives their life manipulating others, he cages himself in a glass box. Inside that box, he can see what he most desires, but he never demonstrates the authenticity to feel it because at a deep level, he knows he's not really giving love or accepting it in return. This denial, this means of guarding oneself, denies oneself of truly living. Of truly loving anyone, least of all themself. For that I felt sad for him. That's the sadness I feel for narcissists, especially for my father in all his calculated, resentful brooding.

Imagine for a moment being a person like my dad. For this moment in time, the authenticity, the openness to feel the affections given to you, or even feel your affections for others, shuts off because deep down you know they're in a relationship with your mask. You've made yourself unreachable by fear from a long-ago pain, and in essence, become unreachable even to yourself.

For a moment in time, I wondered if God, by way of these thoughts, was helping me understand. Helping me forgive. God was showing me that compassion is the seed that, when planted and grown, blossoms with forgiveness in our hearts. Even for those who have wronged us, most of all for those we love.

I thought about all the times I asked my dad to tell me about my grandparents and he gave jaded statements and convoluted short stories. All the ways I tried to connect with him, he evaded. How I got to see pictures of my family on his side was when my mother secretly showed me, shortly before he threw them in our trash.

I thought about the family's lineage of suicide. His mother. His mother's mother. His mother's sister. His nephew. It was most definitely a line. One that deserved looking at. I had the privilege of seeing what my great aunt had felt in a letter my mom had salvaged amongst those mementos hidden from his trashing. She wanted me to have the chance to know them. In reading that letter, I discovered that my great aunt hated herself. She felt herself so inadequate that life was not worth living, much like her sister and her niece. My great-grandmother left life out of a firm desire for independence and sheer will. One that evoked respect and a chill down the spine. The capacity to kill was most definitely there, but it was turned inward, and it was carried down a line.

It made me think. We so often consider inherited traits when it comes to disease and physical features, personality even to some degree. But what if, what if . . . we have spiritual inheritance? What if our traumas and our lifetimes get encoded in our DNA or our spirits and passed down along a line? Simply passed on by patterns of learned behavior in a family? Carried through like a chain of reactions that are hard for each to break because they are a part of a family lineage so long linked that those features are a part of who we are without even knowing.

Perhaps a family carries their own sense of inheritance. If this were true, my maternal family had some overcoming too. I remembered my maternal cousin, Cameron, telling me once that the Huntington's were cursed with bad relationships. It puzzled me at the time, but with that, a thought clicked into place. My grandma was abandoned by her father in her youth, just as her mother had been abandoned by her beau, my mother by hers, me inside by my father. Abandonment was a generational fear planted by the affirmation of that fear. At some point in these cycles, I can't help but wonder, which comes first?

These inheritances were not just tribulations. With a hopeful, empowered perspective, they were lessons. They're fears and pains we are meant to learn from and overcome with a deepening of wisdom. Within these soul-level family lessons, we find a wellspring of progress so powerful that it taps the very depths of our spirit, our mind, even our heart. We all have lines of lessons; family cycles; traumas to be overcome. And as the member who saw these so vividly, I knew that I was built strong enough, awakened enough, wise enough, to be charged with breaking the cycles. I was ready to do it. It wouldn't be easy, but it would be worth the journey, for myself and those whom I could touch. As with all important things, I'd do it with love.

I wanted to recognize and break through barriers, not just for myself, but to heal the hearts of my ancestors who came before me. With prayerful understanding, I sent them the love that they lost. I wanted to give myself what I deserve and have the commitment to learn what that was until I understood what that meant. I intended to make a clearer way for those who come after me, by means of spiritual release. It was my mission to be a beacon to others like us, because it's so important not to feel alone and to know there's a lighted way. I knew it would take diligence and fortitude, but there was no other way to fully live.

Compassion breeds forgiveness. It wasn't until I felt the compassion, the emotional, spiritual trauma of my family's sadnesses that I felt compassion for my father. I felt their wounds, his wounds, and

I understood who he was. How he became. How he lost himself, his heart, his soul. Compassion flowed through me for him in a way that was totally separate of love. It was something greater than that. It made me able to understand why he treated me the way he did. Why he treated my mother how he had. Why he manipulated everyone and didn't love. Because perhaps his life was too much and love was just too far to feel. Too intense among the intensity of all other life. It seemed to me he followed an ancestral chain. But chains present choices too.

To choose to face yourself, to face abuse, instability, in all its ugly faces, takes a spiritual fortitude born of something I can't define beyond mere consciousness and choice. We all face crossroads in our lives that define who we are. Some don't realize how pivotal these junctures are in our pathways' home to ourselves.

But I see them as a walkway with God where He leads the way, with you right there, ready to make the choices by free will. Stay or go, live or die, do or do not, risk or hide. So much in our lives is defined by choice, and we have the power to make them.

God is a Father like that. He guides us to the opportunities to deepen our spirit, our heart, our mind. Be it by a challenge or a grace. Then, he stands back and allows us the will to choose, being there for us if we fall, when we call to Him. His love is consistent. Something to rest in and rely on. Because that's what fathers do.

Life: Papa

It's said that one is not remembered for what they say but how they make others feel. That's the lasting memory my grandfather left in the hearts of a number of people I couldn't begin to count. I couldn't count them, but I could feel his love's magnitude in the life that entered a person's eyes at his memory, the light that entered their heart, their tears, their voice. I know he was special. Special in the way that casts ripples upon the mirroring surface of people's waters within. Quietly transformative with his love.

My memories of my papa are few. It's why these reactions and stories from others mean so much to me. He passed long before I could know him in a grown-up way. But what I remember is this...I remember that my papa would come to visit my mom every single day. He'd always bring a cup of coffee in a styrofoam cup and stay for a good, long talk. I remember his easy, exuberant laughs, and his big sighs. I remember the blue handkerchief that he kept in his back pocket because he was handy like that. He was one of the few left who still used them as they were intended. I remember how he'd cut up my ice cream bar into a bowl on hot summer nights when I was still too young to eat them off the stick. And how he'd make me blueberry pancakes in the morning when we weren't sharing our love for caramel long-john donuts. He had the patience to get up with me in the middle of the night for a snack of an Oreo cookie. He didn't know that I only did that there. He didn't know that my hunger was for those moments between just me and him. Grandma's ritualistically made meal of beef 'n' noodles the nights I was there because I liked it, and Papa made his toast fly out of the toaster and right onto his plate with a proud grin. Because he was inventive like that. We'd go for walks after supper. And on those walks, he taught me to play kick-the-can, just like he did in his youth, and we explored for treasures together. I remember how he smelled of Old Spice and wood and coffee, how his woodshop smelled in its organized disarray. I remember the warm feel of his loose skin and the feel of his hairy arms.

I remember how my mom used to savor the sound of his tires coming up our gravel driveway because she knew someday she wouldn't hear that precious memory anymore. And at the end of those daily visits, as I watched Papa turn and say *goodbye* to my mom, I remember so many days his voice would choke up and quiver with the words, "I *love you.*" Then, that navy blue hanky would come out as he stepped out the door.

As a little girl, I was stricken by this. His measure of love was a deeper, a more open expression than most people possessed or felt the will to share. I knew my papa was a special man for the deep well of love he held in his heart and the humble, earnest will he had to share it.

He'd drive out of town to gather up one group of relatives to see another, to keep their connection strong. He'd drive far out of town simply to take a cousin to lunch. He'd mow the old neighbor lady's yard and meet his friends for coffee and giving. That's the kind of man he was. He saw a need and met it, be it a neighbor, stranger, or friend. Papa was born a farm man, a steady hand, a gentle heart. He held those natures as a father, as a husband, a worker, a neighbor, a friend. He was, all in all, a *man.* The true kind to stand the tests of time.

My papa's love is why men and women to this day emotionally remember his actions, his ways, his heart, his character. It's their hearts remembering that existential measure of love. He was a man whose impact was timeless. One who spread kindness, wisdom, joy, and strength to so many places in his world . . . acts of love I could only wish to truly know. That's the kind of man my papa was.

My last memory of my papa was when I last saw him breathing, in the years when he could no longer speak. His crystal blue eyes looked straight through my own, and his hand squeezed mine three times. I. Love. You.

Life: Love in Lines

We all come from lines. Some distant, some near. Some we earnestly follow in the footsteps of. Some we let fall away. Some choose to follow for lack of conscious awareness or will. Others we have the strength of will and wisdom to break. Who we are and how we live within our family lineage all comes down to choice. The line I've chosen is love. Because it's inherently me. It was my mother. It was my grandfather. It was my great grandmother too. All connected by the line. Empowered by the love that passes down from heart to heart.

My mother taught me . . .

. . . that love is selfless, like her love.

Love feels like flying.

Love is kind, in words and thoughts.

Love gives hope and keeps promises.

Love carries you forward when you've lost your way.

Love listens and is tender.

Love sees you, the parts of you that so often go unseen.

Love understands and tries and cares earnestly without ending.

Love is a sense of giving without taking away. But in taking, taking in.

Love surprises and keeps secrets solely to fill the heart with the knowing that they're thought of always; that they're special.

Love keeps a memory to last beyond the leagues of time. It follows the trail of the heart.

Love continues like a journey.

Love is a hard nudge to follow and a soft place to land.

Love is effortful and effortless.

Love knows no bounds.

Love carries no record of fallacy or malign.

Love holds strong to the truth, even when it's difficult.

Love is pure. In its essence and in its ways. To love is to be love.

It's a way of living and it's who we emanate to be.

That's what my mother taught me about love. And without her, I'd never have learned to fly.

Life: Reasons, Seasons, Lifetimes

All good things serve a purpose and a time. I'd venture to say for that reason, all things may be harnessed into good, with the right perspective. The best of things come into our lives for a very special purpose. One that lights a fire within our soul, illuminates our minds. Transmutes light from darkness, enriches each new day, makes you think in a way you never thought before. These are the *reasons.* They're meant to guide us, fuel us, and if you look closely, you'll see that somehow you do the same for them. God works that way. It's beautiful. It's His art. Of Love. For us.

One of our great mysteries of this life is how much time we may have with certain things. People, places, occupations, outlets, possessions, lessons of life. These *seasons* are harder to judge. They're harder to judge because they're not meant to be judged. The mere act of judging them can spoil the very essence of living them.

Sometimes, seasons are a powerful, brief glimmer of hope; sheer force by a moment in a lifetime. Other times, a season could be a long stay, one that lingers in the heart when it goes. Regardless of their length, seasons can be hard to break from because they become tied to the heart.

It's because God pairs seasons and reasons together. They're part of the cohesion of life. Seasons linger because they make a lasting impression on the heart, the mind, even the spirit. And time, no matter how long or short it seems to be, can't take that impression away. It's everlasting. Honor it. You don't have to let it go. A seed was planted. Let it grow.

Lifetimes seem to go without saying. They are those you can depend on without end. You'll know them deeply when you find them, and they will not leave your side. For they grant you unconditional love. Yes. It does exist. Here and on the other side. Without end. They're a blessing I am thankful for every single day. You must be too, whether you have it now or it's a dream that's on its way. Growing from the roots of love you hold for yourself.

I believe every love that comes into our lives is meant for a reason, a season, or a lifetime. Which love is yours, you might ask? Each is a gift from God. Each molds us into a better, brighter person as we walk with Him. I believe every reason, season, and lifetime is planted for me. And I am ever grateful as I grow.

Reflection: **Mysterious Journeys**

When I bike, my favorite route to take is a route unknown. Turning down a road I've never been and seeing where it takes me. If the route turns out like the one I chose yesterday, those roads lead to fields of wildflowers, where the pavement turns to gravel and my tires stir up hundreds of tiny butterflies that softly brush my sunkissed arms bringing a pure smile to my face as they burst into the illuminating skyline, drawing my focus up to the gentle sounds of joyous song-birds and the beautiful face of a doe standing just yards before me as she peacefully ponders disappearing into the forest once again. Rides like these feed the soul, filled with the awe of what I view as loving gifts from above. There's a challenge in pushing against the wind up the inclines of the hills, making me dig deep for strength and endurance, but the discovery that lies at every peak and valley of those hills makes that challenge satisfying, fueling, breathtaking.

Other rides down these mysterious roads are less romantic. They may have inviting wildflowers and a long and winding lane, but as I enter, a feeling of disillusionment already settles somewhere in my consciousness. I proceed with curious optimism. As I travel down this road, the beauty of the landscape draws me in. I travel farther seeing where it leads until I find myself assaulted by a fly, then another and another until I realize I must ride full speed to ward off full-on attack. Suddenly, the beautiful road ends in the form of a rouge metal gate with remnants of a padlock hanging off a rusted old chain. Beyond that, thick woods. I turn my bike around while simultaneously thwarting off my small following and proceed back to the main road to return home. I don't regret going down this road. It was pretty for a while, but as my instinct told me, there were things hiding in those beautiful flowers that could pack a bite and the path led to an eerie dead end. All is fair in the game of country roads. It's part of the adventure.

Both of these experiences are completely real, every minute detail, but they struck me as metaphoric of navigating the pathways to love. On the wrong road, that off gut feeling is the first sign followed by some beauty which is a very brief illusion. Then the flies are the warning signs that multiply and nag you though you may proceed, telling you something isn't right and will hurt you. The padlock, perhaps a lock on someone's heart. The dead end, just that. In contrast, the right road has the butterflies. Those butterflies are the little moments when a person makes you feel alive, inspired, touched, cared for in a new and real way. The little things they say and do that bring an infectious smile to your face. The songbirds like the sound of their voice and their words that speak to both your mind and your heart. The doe, someone's vulnerability, so beautifully revealing themselves to you in full form amazingly, touchingly with little trepidation. This road goes on and on. Over time, it becomes a little less exhilarating but rather calming and comforting with moments of surprise as I ride along, something I find equally fulfilling and also metaphoric of time spent in love. The wind and hills represent the fact that this beautiful awe-striking road isn't easy. It takes hard work and effort, and commitment. Without that, those discoveries would not be made, and the beauty of that road and its journey would be lost.

Which road are we? I wonder to myself. *Are we a road of tiny but-terflies? Or are we one that has a gate at the end?* I keep both hands on my handlebars and breathe in each discovery, keeping my senses open. And as I take each day as it comes, I enjoy the ride down this road with my friend.

Life: Love Illuminates

On a brisk late afternoon, the light was low and yet a yellow cascade of color fell from the hackberry trees, giving flight to their warty leaves. I took my bike on my usual ride through the park outside of town. Riding my laps around its loop gave me the dose of nature my spirit craved and the workout my body asked for. It was a hidden treasure in central Illinois, endowed by a well-to-do farmer's wife with a mission to give back to the community. I remember my mother's stories of taking a school field trip to the homestead of Ms. Violet Scully. She invited kindergarteners each year to her scrolling land so that in-town children could experience what farm life was like. Milk a cow, see the stables, sit in her tearoom and drink a cup with her. Hearing those stories, I can feel the joy Violet received from her giving. Just as the park was an extension of her giving that continued into my day today. The treasure she gave our town wasn't lost on me. Nor was the care taken in preserving it by its cheerful park ranger who never failed to grant his patrons a cheerful wave as we passed him by. It was the best kept park in town, likely because it was private, and because of him

As I rounded my first lap of my usual six in its circular drive through the trees, I came upon a small-statured man, lean with a blue knitted hat pulled low across his face to meet a closely trimmed brown beard. The kind of scruff that made him feel more manly and soft at the same time. He was walking a black lab and carried himself like he knew how to be a man and be sensitive too. Like he was a real person, a deep person, with backwoods or country friends he spent Saturday night with to frame his quiet weekday evenings. Who hung that hat in a home set for one man yet somehow cozy. A homemade where his boots rested continually by the door and he drank his coffee strong. In that moment of whizzing by him, I just had time to lift my hand in a wave, and simultaneously his did too. When his hand lifted, there was meaning in that gesture. In that moment, I felt as though a lifetime of knowing played across my memory, struck right through my spirit like a bell. I looked back, and I could see that his head had turned down and back discreetly. I couldn't help but wonder, did he feel that other-worldly moment too? I could best describe it as a connection. I felt a connection with this man that I had never felt towards any stranger or passerby, and I could not explain why. I just knew that it meant something. When I had these feelings in my spirit, my heart followed them like a hound on the scent.

I pedaled faster on my bike to make it around to the other side, not knowing where his trail would end. When I made it around, he was gone. How could that be? I had covered all the ground. I'd even looked on the side inlets as I passed to be certain. I sighed. Must not have been meant to be. I passed my bike through the park for the rest of my usual laps and then made my way to the outlet which led to the main highway, or in my case, the lower service road that I took to get home. As I pushed up the hill past the last parking spaces near the entrance, there he was, helping his dog into a little blue truck. He walked around the other side and got in. He started it up and turned left out of the park. I pedaled hard to see where it would go, but the truck disappeared beyond the overpass. Maybe he lived on that side of town, perhaps out of town all together. I'd never seen him or his truck before, so either could be true. I was almost certain he felt what I did in that moment, but something told me he wasn't one to act on it. He hadn't. Maybe he had a reason. Nevertheless, my spirit felt something big, and it wasn't ready to let it go that easily.

For weeks after that moment, I kept my eye out for that little blue truck. In parking lots, on the road, but especially at the park. I even tried to go there around that time again, but I never caught one glimpse of the man with the dog or that little blue truck. Eventually as my search faded into months, it submitted to not-meant-to-be fate. I chalked it up to an inexplicable provoking . . . moment. But it was more than that, so much more.

Life: The Heart's First Fall

Historically speaking, I've tended to be pretty strict with myself when it comes to diet and exercise. Being at a healthy weight makes me feel better about myself. Feeling better about myself makes me a smidge easier on myself in the privately critical recesses of my mind. That's incentive enough for me to stay fit and have a salad for lunch on workdays. The highlight of teaching just blocks from my home was that I got to eat lunch with my mother on those thirty-minute periods. We'd catch up on each other's mornings and enjoy a cup of coffee together as we sat at the breakfast nook table that looked out over the canopy of small maple trees in the neighbor's yard. It was one of millions of acts of love my mother did for me, setting that stage every day at noon for us to share a meal together, picking me up to save some time. Our kindred conversation was easy, and the cherished minutes passed always too quickly before she had to take me back to my little family of children that were finishing their minutes of recess, save the few who awaited my return to share their recess time with me, excitedly bouncing up and down when they saw the car at the corner. Time together was precious to us all.

Over and over again, I began to hear a new trend in my mother's weekly routines. A name being mentioned each week. It was her produce man. At first, I simply listened with interest but as the time went on, I began to look forward to the weekly installments of her interactions with this attentive man who made a point to speak with her whenever she came in. People in their thirties didn't often have time for customers that way, let alone making sure she had my red leaf lettuce as fresh and well stocked as we needed. His special attention and care for her nourished a growing appreciation in me for who he was.

In the weeks that Mom didn't mention him, I found myself inquiring about her grocer. And she said that he inquired about me. Enough that I could tell he somehow wondered like I did. He even mentioned the notion of me coming with her sometime. I imagined him wondering if I was anything like her. Any young man who was smart enough to see my mom for who she was would ask that.

Who was this person being so kind to my mom? I had to meet him just to thank him for being so good to her in this world. So, I accompanied her when next she went.

When I walked in the store, Levi immediately set down what he was doing and walked straight to me. He was nervous. We talked easily. I couldn't tell you what about because my memory doesn't serve me for my own nervousness. He asked me for my number and went to the back to get a pen, writing it down on a piece of cardboard that I wondered if he'd lose track of, but sure enough when he got off work, he texted me. The best thing I can tell you to describe the way he spoke in texts, calls, visits, anything, was that he was different. In every way. In a good way.

Reflection: Paper Wasp

The process paper wasps go through making their nest is much like how a heart makes a home. First, it must find the perfect safe location to build from. For a wasp, a tree limb beneath the shade of leaves. For a heart, on the shoulder of one who will stay there. One who will see and feel and hear and love. Ardently. This takes discernment, some would say through experience. Others would look back upon the wasp and know there's a deeper instinct that drives us to our highest needs if we listen and let it.

Next comes the hard work. Once we have found that proper location to rest our hearts, build the home of our hearts, we must know that home needs walls. A safety net from the world around. Isn't that the great haven home is?

The paper wasp is a steady creature. Intent on building. The process by which a paper wasp goes and retrieves mouthfuls of wood fibers to return them in kind to their nest for homemaking is something of an art. They go out into the world and take something rough and soddened and transform it. They make it entirely new in preparation of a home. Creating soft pulp, their masses of work become delicate, intricate layers of a naturally made paper. Sheets that swirl with texture and curl around one another as a solid unit. A one-piece design made of a million fruitful labors. Labors of protection. Labors of love.

The heart is much the same. A person goes out into the world and brings with them many hard, soddened experiences that can be transformed into something soft and new. Something worthy of building a life from, protecting a heart with. Wisdom, feelings, prayers, and dreams, whether they're one and the same or all in all, are meant to be shared steadily with care. They're the building of the nest. The walls that two can create around their hearts to protect and make a sweet haven from the world and nest within. Cherish each other more with every thin layer. For within the art of building, what's in those intricate walls is trust, respect, knowing, hearing, care, sincerity, hope, and dimensions of each other found between layers that no outside world may ever see or know but two can revere. You're building a home for two hearts to be safe in each other, enveloped by each other from the world. For within the art of building what's in those intricate walls is the art of making Love.

Life: **Pickup**

The night of our first date, I watched out the picture window waiting for him to pick me up. Finally, headlights came into the early evening view. A little blue Dodge truck turned onto my brick street. As it slowly approached the curb of my neighbor's house, I blinked back a spellbound flicker of wondering. It had been years since I'd seen the truck at the park. So much had passed since then, I'd long let it go.

Pushing the thought out of my mind, I could see his head ducking to peer at the house. He slowly drove up to mine, and I was almost out the door when he turned down the little side road, backing up and looking all around as if he were a lost pup. Back down the street he drove as I unbolted the door, and just as I reached the curb, he'd turned onto another. He must've been looking back all the while because that little blue truck instantly flipped into reverse. He made his way to me.

By the time he reached my drive, I was standing ankle crossed, and knee bent, arms folded, wearing a playful grin. When I stepped inside onto his old native sheet covered seat, it was plain to see he was embarrassed.

"I shouldn't get frustrated. But I did." He wanted it to go well, and in his eyes that moment hadn't.

He'd begun our relationship as any ought to, as friends. He brought me for a walk with his parents and their dogs along their avenue and streets. The walk with his parents was easy, with his jovial mom and quiet father. All through town and the park conversation flowed. But I noticed one thing, and his mom saw it too. Levi was entirely and tightly wound in his shell.

Sliding back into his truck to take me back home, Levi paused with his hand on the clutch. "I don't know why I acted like that. You're so nice. I didn't need to do that. It was just different. I don't know. I just don't know. My parents really liked you." He slowly put the truck in gear, leaving the curb. "Yeah, they enjoyed you a lot. They would. I just didn't have anything to say, I guess." The more he talked the more he re-entered his moment of nerves, becoming frustrated with himself. It hurt me to see him feel this way. I had to stop him right there.

"Levi, I enjoyed our walk. Your parents are fun people, and I'm glad you brought me along with you. Thank you. Don't put so much pressure on yourself. Just being around you brings me joy." In an instant his mind was at ease. On the ride home, we chatted and laughed in an easy way that mattered. It made the late afternoon sun shine right into my heart.

He was anxious but in a way that gave me a safe place. For in his unsureness I found a place to express the unfiltered, open care and concern for someone that I'd long ago learned to contain. Contain for the sake of not falling prey in the game of love. Don't show too much care or they'll capitalize and see it as weakness; as an invitation to take advantage of your kind and open heart. No, here in this man's world there was no game to strain my downtrodden heart. In that regard, I was safe. One hundred percent.

That night on my back patio after he walked me up the drive, goodbye was more than words. It was a shyness in his handsome face, a sparkle in his blue eyes. He kissed me with respect and passion.

Life: Illuminating Walk

We went for a walk in the late afternoon after the heat of the day had turned into the warmth of the night. We were gifted with the rarity that was a chilly breeze in what had become the annual Indian summer in our neck of the heartland. Different from the fall season we remembered from our youth yet somehow just right for the occasion because it kept us in company actively outdoors, just as we liked best. I'd been waiting for him on my front porch steps, kicking off with a start the moment his blue truck turned into view. The sound of its tires rolling down the bricks of our road had become a sound of coming adventure. Hopping onto that old native blanket, taking in a breath of fresh air that was his sparkling grin, his shy blush and fumble that always followed. It enamored me, just as I enamored him in some philosophical, poetic way.

Now, we were among the golden leaves. Long brown pods from the honey locust tree and the puff bombs off the sycamore adorned the ground among the leaves, bringing a lifetime of childhood memories flooding to my senses. The earthy aroma of their autumn display cleansed my spirit as we walked in quiet together. Talking but often not needing words. That was something he so often said he appreciated about us. I think a part of him felt he wasn't good with words, but I would beg the contrary. His words showed a measure of quality of quantity with some unexpected moments of poignant candor that were unmistakably magic to me.

As we walked in silence, he took my hand nervously, commenting that mine might be cold, but when he held it, he was sure. I smiled to myself, to the trees beyond us. I was happy. Happy flowed through my every fiber. A surge went right through me when he took my hand. It was a moment that seemed to take me from one reverie right into the reality of another; one memory that'd been pushed from my mind. The brisk late afternoon. The golden canopy all around us of changing hackberry trees. This very pavement as we approached a little blue truck in the very parking spot it rested in those years ago. My awareness of him walking next to me became more real as my eyes casted up from my path to him. The handsome face with a chiseled, soft scruff. The masculine step. The frame. I was living out the very picture I'd felt those years ago. The realization of the past and present becoming one settled into my bones in one vivid awe of actualization.

Life: The Beginning

Some women may have seen his insecurity as weakness, but I saw a part of him to hold tenderly. To nurture. I assured him in all his nervousness. He needed encouragement that he was good and well. I respected the way he held humility rather than egotism. For better or worse, all his fear helped me find a sense of trust that he wasn't malicious; that he wouldn't hurt me. But also I realized that in his fear, he could break my heart.

Every love is a risk of heartbreak. We must choose to let our heart lead anyway, because its higher wisdom calls us where we're meant to grow. It's a pathway of discovery, for a reason, a season, or a lifetime. If we don't follow our heart, we don't fully live the life we are called to. So, I reasoned to water it, tend to it, and watch it grow. We both did that.

Life: Another Evening

Levi and I shared a love for the outdoors, for movement. It calmed us both, made us both feel more alive and connected to nature. On warm sunny evenings, he'd send me a message, arrive a few minutes late, and we'd be on our way. Respectful as he was, I knew late arrivals came from his scattered, anxious nature. In that, I knew my waiting wasn't a sign of disregard, and that made it okay. I waited. And as times passed, I was sorry for the evenings growing late only for the time lost together. What made his late arrivals more okay was how wonderful it was when he arrived.

This night, he sent me a message asking when he might pick me up. I told him I was ready for him. And he replied saying he'd cooked dinner and was about to hop in the shower and then he'd swing by.

"I'll be ready with my mystery dessert." I replied.

"Ha, I can't wait." I could see his smile in his voice on the other end of the line.

I waited on the curb, pie in hand. When he pulled up, he was visibly moved by the fact that I'd made his favorite.

"Peee-can pie. I can't believe you made pecan pie. I thought you were bringing cookies or brownies or something. That makes me feel real good inside. Wow."

I touched his shoulder and told him, "You've been working all day and then you came home and made dinner all yourself. That is so sweet of you, Levi. You didn't have to do that, how very kind of *you.*"

He'd taken great care in his meal preparations. I acknowledged his perfectly cut fries and vegetables, his organized baking tray, clean kitchen, and always cozy home. It was clear he'd made sure everything was just right. He shrugged his shoulders and chuckled, unsure what to say. He met my eyes, he smiled, looked down, and blushed. It touched me. I took in that moment.

He told me that he admires how I treat people so kindly and with such care. He said he was in awe that my care and kindness for the world never falters. That there's an innocence in me that says I've always been this way, admitting he hadn't. His appreciation for who I am humbled me in that moment.

He nervously checked the potatoes. But as he'd already described, it was a good sort of nervous, the kind that he called excited and I'd call stepping outside of your comfort zone. I looked at him, taking in the moment, the feeling. He looked down at the pie, cheeks as rosy as a schoolboy.

We ate dinner in his living room to one of the movies we both loved as kids. When the credits rolled, I braced myself for him to get up and remove the disc from his player, but he didn't move a muscle. Slowly moving my eyes so as not to disturb, I looked over at him. His were closed, his face relaxed in an expression of peace. We sat like that with our heads together for the longest time until we shared a few small kisses and lay down on the couch. I could tell that again he was making sure the moment wasn't ruined, even by the slightest act of moving, his legs off the couch. So much careful thought in the man. After a time, he pulled them up onto the couch and we laid there side by side for hours, him just holding me, me holding him. I fell asleep in his arms.

As he drove me home, out of the darkness came, "I can't believe you made me a pecan pie." He marveled out into the darkness of the night road. "Thank you so much. For the pie, for having dinner with me, the movie, more than that, thank you for just being with me. Thank you for being with me tonight, Allie." He pulled me into a meaningful hug.

I watched as he did a happy long skip as he walked back down my driveway, reflecting that happy skip in my chest.

Life: **Romance**

After dinner in our own homes, he picked me up to visit. I helped him clean his kitchen. Sometimes this helped him get his nerves out when I first arrived. It seemed like he put pressure on himself for things to be perfect or something of that sort. It gave him the jitters. We did the dishes together in the kitchen while we talked about our days. I knew one of Levi's greatest little frustrations was getting stuck with dish duty. Every. Time. The little things do really matter a lot. Washing his dishes when I was there was my attempt to relieve that, ease it for him even for that day. He'd get stuck in his frustration talking about it, something that sometimes happened when he was alone, but soon later he'd run to the basement to pick up some foil and he'd be singing up the steps like no one was watching. I loved when he did that.

Relaxed and duty free, we sat on his couch and talked in the dark of his living room by the glow of the light from the kitchen. Time like this was a joy for me because though we didn't always need words, words were always heard when we shared them. That's what I loved most about our talks.

When I spoke, he listened. Like no one had listened before. He listened to my heart. He listened to my soul. Anything I said to him fell on hearing ears. Knowing ears, and it felt so good. I loved sharing my passions with him, and when I shared my pains, he could barely take it. Because he was right there too. Feeling. It was like finding a piece of myself in him.

That night on the couch he loved me like no other man had before. He never once tried to lift my shirt, nor did I so much as once have to give quiet reminder to groping hands that we were still new. No, these hands touched me, rather his hands, his head, arms, fingertips touched me with a tenderness, a reverence, an echo of love that I'd never felt before. The sensation gave me a long moment of awareness when I was engulfed in taking in the present. In what this man had in his heart to give to me. Did anyone ever see this man? "This is what it feels like." I told myself. "I know he doesn't love me, but this is what it feels like to be loved." I was more than just a body to him. Sure, there was an obvious attraction, but it stemmed deeper than that. He saw deeper than that. He was loving me. All of me. And what felt good to him was feeling my spirit. He softly kissed my forehead, my lips. His fingertips grazed along my arm, and he leaned his head into my neck in what could best be described as a soulful nuzzle. He wrapped his arms around me and sighed, resting his head on my chest. Even the way he held me framed a picture of sincerity. When he held me, he did as if he didn't want to let go. Everywhere his skin touched mine sent a soft tinge quietly in me. His eyes held a serious gaze. Gone was the unconfident man, for he too was wrapped up in this moment that could best be described as simply, purely: romantic.

Life: It Goes On

He'd message me to plan our outings together, most always a walk in the evening. "I think you should leave the second you can tomorrow." he sent once. "Race the kids out of class. It's three weeks to Thanksgiving, and I think the weather is finally about perfect. Crazy!"

His suggestion sparked a sense of value inside of me. Putting myself first that way hadn't occurred to me before. It had always felt very uncomfortable. But something about his words, because of him, I threw it all aside, "You know what, you're right! Honestly, in all my Fridays of teaching, I've never left early. But this time I will! I'll bolt out of there at 3:15. That's a promise!"

"You have got to live a little Allie. Treat yourself tomorrow and leave a little earlier than you would. What can't wait till later? Tomorrow works fine for me. We can go after you get home from school. If you do have to stay longer that's fine, I really have nothing but time."

And I made a point to leave on time that day. I made a point to leave on time, and not feel guilty for giving extra of myself. I gave that time to me, to us. It made me feel worth more, even to myself as I stepped out that door to see him for our walk.

He looked at me in the sunlight as we wandered through the prairie, and he started to say something, and then stopped. "What is it?" I asked him, taking him in as I did.

" . Well, I was just looking at your eyes. You can see them really good out here. It's kind of like looking down from Heaven. Like you're looking through the sky and the clouds and the trees in all the colors."

Life: Nerves

After work one night, he took me to the state park. We had the place to ourselves. I hadn't placed my feet on those grounds since I was a little girl. It looked new to me again. Then again, I think the company we keep brings out the beauty in things.

We sat on the creek bank and shared bits of our past, reflecting just like the sun on its surface but opening up like the bend on its way. I could tell from his presence there was an aggressive side in there from his remembrances, but it takes two to fight. And I was versed in assuaging anger. It felt appealingly familiar amidst his respectfully, tender spirit.

As we made our way back through the wooded path, he was different. He held an intensity that I had not yet seen before, off kilter in a way that made me on alert. It was like an energy was surging through him that he was working to contain. He began to speak in bits here and there. I could tell it had to do with a thought that had plagued him for some time. "I want a wife and children. I really want that and think it would make me happy in life. You're more than I ever thought I could have. You're so gentle and you have such a good heart. You're so patient with me. You're perfect. But sometimes I don't think I'm built for that. I've been on my own for so long and maybe it's easier to keep it that way."

Scattered statements spewed as he shared his feelings with me, how much I made him feel and how good he felt about himself and life with me in it, and I quietly took them in from a small distance as we walked. Every word was caught up in the angst of pushing away. "I feel you. I feel you getting in. And it hurts. It hurts to be apart, to need you, and it makes me feel weak. So, I go to work out. I push you out of my head because then I can feel strong again, like I don't need anyone. But sometimes that doesn't work and I'm even more frustrated."

He cursed. "I want you, but I don't want to need you. My life is fine like it is. I'm a lone wolf. You take me out of that. Sometimes I think I'm always gonna be a lone wolf, that being alone is better for me. I don't know. It feels so good to be around you. You make me feel so good, you're so patient with me and so kind, you make me feel that. But I don't want to need that."

I listened as he surged through his innermost thoughts until at once, perhaps for my quiet listening, he was frustrated with me directly. He assumed I was judging him, that I'd be bothered, mad that we weren't committed. I sensed this was what he must have been used to. My calm and simple reply was this. "I have enjoyed getting to know you and spending time with you. I think you are a special person. But if a relationship is not something you want, then I can respect that." And I did. It hurt, what he'd said, but I could see that he held fierce tensions within, and I felt that needed grace.

His moments of silence spoke of the weight of my words, the choice before him, and the one I had already made. "Alright, alright Allie, I'm just going to shut up. I'm just going to stop." I wished he wouldn't talk to himself so harshly. I wondered what he wanted, but I knew he wondered too, so I let him stop.

He left me unsure. By the time we got to the highway, he was softer. Apologetic. His fire not fed, had died out, and he was once again himself. I smiled softly back at him in reserve. Still, when mom asked me how our visit went, I simply replied, "It was nice being out at the park." A lot was on my mind.

Life: Push, Pull

As romantic as our feelings were, there was this major flaw in our growing friendship. Levi told me he wanted me but yet he wouldn't make room in his life for me. I'd grown familiar with late arrivals, but it was the limits on our time together that puzzled and hurt me. He just didn't think of me at times. How do you care and yet have that person escape your mind? I couldn't count on him to always show up when he said he would. Sometimes he forgot about a date he made entirely. This was such an odd contrast to what I experienced when his walls broke down, when I saw him and he let himself look at me. It was confusing for the beginning of this connection we had, the chemistry. It made me careful.

In our next night together, we spoke of his feelings. I wanted to learn him, to understand. I wanted him to know that his feelings mattered. I learned how he lost his confidence years ago and never got it back, swore off relationships after one gone wrong. How he found his way back to himself, alone, and he felt safe there. He didn't like change, that was a sure thing. But I was a good change, he said, a change that made him better. In so many words, he told me that with me in his life, he sees a different picture of what he wants and it changes everything. That's not just change, that's a big change, an adjustment to even the routine of daily living. Something he resists more than anyone.

"Levi, it seems you need to make a choice. If you feel even a tinge of resistance, you may think you know what you want but really you are on the fence. You need to do some soul searching as to what you truly want for yourself and for your life."

"How do you do soul searching?" he replied softly. Whether he was asking me or putting the question out to the void, I gave him the best answer I knew from my heart.

"Ask yourself why? Therein lies the answer. Why do I want this? Why don't I want that? But whatever choice you come to needs to be with your whole heart."

He nodded, staring at the wall across the room. "You really know how to help someone work through anything."

His eyes looked like he needed a bit more, so I continued deeper. "In life, I believe we are set out on different trajectories. Within those paths we have choices, and that's the freedom of will. That free will is what gives us the branches to our tree of life." I was reluctant to lean any of my words my way for the sake of not influencing his choice. If he chose me, it had to come from him and only him. It wouldn't be right any other way. It could never last any other way. Tonight, he seemed to insist on wanting to embrace the change of me in his life, but I insisted he think and really know.

"Thank you Allie. You've really helped me."

When he began to apologize again, I redirected the conversation telling him all I thought of him. I didn't want him to get down on himself.

His smile crinkled his eyes as his shoulders turned in a bit to smile themselves. "You can really say words to make a person feel good."

Life: La La Night

We planned a night at the movies. It felt good going out in public with him. He wasn't shy about it at all like I thought he may be. He felt quietly mine, and I his. It felt nice.

We were the only two in the theater. Choosing seats near the top row, it felt exciting and comforting simply to be close to him. His nervous, sweet smile. "Cinescope" sprawled across the screen, and I felt every nuance of the film. Taking it in was an artful sensory experience. Romantic, even with the tension between us. He never held my hand or threw an arm around me like the stereotypical movie guy moves. I think he was too shy, which was all the more endearing to me, even if I wanted him to. Instead, he tapped his feet to the tunes in an infectious way I wished I felt free enough to be. Just the same way that he sang through the house like no one was watching.

As I sat there in that movie theater watching what would become one of my favorite films, I didn't yet realize that its lasting message would speak to me for him: people come into our lives for a reason. They mirror us, they validate us, change us, shake our spirit, break us down so we can rebuild stronger. All those things he did for me.

But in that night, as we stepped out of the back door of our local theater, strikingly like Gosling and Stone's scene in the show, his hand warmed mine. We made our way to his truck to take in our shared joy for the Christmas lights' glow. I can still see him pausing midstep, arm reaching back, his muscular hand opening for mine. It's one of those memories that etch into your mind's eye for safe keeping in your heart. It rests next to the image of those hands turning the steering wheel left and right as we wound up and down the streets, lights twinkling in our eyes as we passed the hours opening our hearts. Our youths, our triumphs, understandings, desires, and fears, his secrets, my pains. Though I shared far more than he it seemed, that's what was right. For me it was natural. This level of openness seemed uncharted territory for him. Still, the vulnerability, at any measure, did us both good. Almost as much as sharing our unique love for one of life's simple joys in that chilly glow.

He ended by showing me his favorite home that his dad always drove them by each Christmas when he and his siblings were children. At 76 years old, the man was still putting on his display with unmeasured passion. Somehow, I wished I could knock on his door and thank the man. For the special memory he gave that family and to me. The magic between us, it was shared in these moments. It was shared in the appreciation of this man and his public act of kindness. All the people like him in the world. Our magic was in our shared joy over the small things in life. Alone, those things were special to us. But somehow, in this fast, unseeing world, that joy made magic when we found it together.

Love is effortless and effortful. It comes in a breath and never leaves the spirit. It begs of you to allow it, to share it.

Reflection: The Infinite Shape of Love

I took a walk, reflecting on the balance of love. What it looks like, feels like, and how it ought to be. What I wanted to carry with me moving forward into life.

Two eagles soared into view, dancing in reverie. Weaving together and apart in infinity, their graceful dance spoke of romance. A glancing eye would spy them apart as one drifts away from the other. But in magical unison, they find their way back again. Perfect harmony forming broad figure eights.

Even my enamored eye would barely perceive those vast forms of infinity traced upon the sky were it not for the invisible cord that seemed to draw them right back to each other. Drawing them so close it could only speak of Love. This pair spoke of how love is held together and apart. Expression without reserve, trust without boundaries, yet longing as if an invisible cord strung the two together. Always in reverie. Soaring together, they disappeared into the skyline, leaving me to absorb the power of love in its greatest form, as God shows us in His way.

Their soliloquy struck me as they drifted to and fro into the skyline, leaving me in awe of their meaning of Love. Their soliloquy spoke of many things. Love in its most powerful form is together and apart. Because Love has this reverie. It has the power of unified separation bound with a different measure of Love. A Love that watches with the heart's eye yet glides with the independent spirit as it casts its course. To gloriously be pulled back in again by that undeniable, invisible cord of soul. Each recognizing their own mate. Knowing that when they part, they'll be together again. Always. And again.

It spoke of the empowering freedom of independence in abounding love. Casting one's own light upon the wind and the space that's needed to maintain it. It spoke touchingly of returning, fueled by their own course, only to be fueled by each other once again.

Across the sky, their infinite dance painted a story of faith, each bird riding its own steering wind to such far distances apart that a bystander would ne'er notice the pair. It spoke of faith in togetherness. Faith that Love does not run astray but comes back Home again. And again. That "wherever our journeys take us, you'll return to me again, just as I am drawn to you. You were on your way back to me as you set out on your own, just as I to you. I know because our spirits, our souls, are bound by the chord of our hearts' song. Again and again and again."

They deepened my faith in knowing that this kind of Love between two kindred spirits has the boundlessness to allow perfect balance. Independence that is so needed and the aching, soaring, graceful Love that makes them fall right back into each other. They can't help but Love so immensely that nothing for long keeps them away. Heart, mind, soul. Love comes in all forms. But I know this one was a glimmer of my own. Be it here on this Earth or destined to be held in the sky. A dream of a heart's song. And again.

Life: Love's Light and Shadow

Love is in the details. Be it a shared task, a little favor, an act of grace, a note of expression. Those little things speak with power. Love too, is found in the details of a man: his never-changing authenticity, recognizing it and appreciating it in kind. His ability to be in awe, and in touch with the world outside himself. It's the details about a person that come together to make them the person who is loved.

In Levi, it was the old-fashioned way he walked me to the door and could barely tear himself away from goodbye, the way he watched me from his rearview window taking me in as he slowly drove away from our lunch dates, the moments he'd pour his heart and soul out to me with unfiltered earnestness that left me breathless in awe, the tender way he touched me that spoke of electric desire tempered by reverent respect. I guess like the old country tune, I loved the way he loved me.

It was love that pinched me with hurt as I told him no when he eventually asked me out again. And it was all the little details that I loved in him. It was those details that haunted me when we parted. What we had was messy but special, and I missed it. I felt drawn to him like an urge I could resist less and less with each passing month that went by.

When I saw him yet again, it was easy as it ever was, like we'd never parted. Easing back into where we left off was like slipping into a rhythm charged with energy, life, albeit frustration. Some nights, he was tense or uneasy to be near. That was the nature of it. It was a part of him I enveloped with love. I could see what he did to himself within, and he simply needed love. Most of all for himself. I wanted to help him find that.

Those nights when our time together just flowed, it was easy. I floated away from those evenings and held them in my heart. But more often than not, he was as nervous as a cat in a room full of rocking chairs. He liked to say that he wasn't anxious, that his tension was excitement. Either way, I helped him wash his day away along with his tension as we did his dishes and talked. It felt like breaking through one layered wall after another until finally he would be himself again. No longer edgy from his day, no longer bursting. There was a dance that needed done to bring peace to his heart. And I was rewarded with the gift of seeing him feel loved, be easy with himself.

The greatest dance between us was the rhythm of us. Like the night when we shared our likes in music, which romantically fell in sync just like the footsteps of our reverie as our foreheads met and our embrace entranced a slow and gentle stepping to and fro of nothing else in the world but us. In that moment, I realized, no matter what song was on, what was around us, the only thing in the world was him, this feeling, and me.

I was able to share my thoughts and feelings with him like no other place. He listened with quiet, unadulterated interest, and his eyes were open to heart's passions. I shared my deepest beliefs about life, which somehow grounded them all the more to find a soul to relate them to. I shared my loves for my students and worries for them, stories left untold that never went unappreciated in his arms on the couch. He shared in them all through investing in me, truly seeing me. Past my face, through my heart, and right into my spirit. That's what it felt like when we talked. And when he shared stories of his life, what made this man with me, it was just the same. Open, raw, discreet, and real. But his secrets I will not tell. We're too good of friends for that.

One night, as his rough fingertips were grazing over my soft forearm in a slow, tingling rhythm, he looked up at me across in the darkness of his living room. He told me, "You make people feel like they're worth something and you love everyone and see the good in everyone. You make people feel like they matter. And you're beautiful. But it's not just that. It's not your features or your form. It's your spirit. You feel like a Mother Teresa. And it's not just sometimes; you're that way consistently, always. You treat everyone the same, everyone you meet. Always, every time. It never stops. I've never met someone like you. It's special. But I don't think you see that, you're not into yourself, which makes you more beautiful."

Life: Valentine

I woke up one morning in February to a message from him. It read as follows.

"Good morning Miss Allie,
Be careful as you open the door,
What could it be,
For whom I adore.
You came into my life on my special day,
Here is a little something
For you on your day.
Thanks Allie, for you.
Happy Valentine's
I did get hungry a bit. It was supposed to be a whole bag."

Dually perplexed and enamored, I toed down the stairs and straight out the back door to find a pot of sunflowers on the back steps in the morning dawn. A partially eaten bag of brownie brittle was tucked under the leaves. I carried them in like they were porcelain less because they were fragile and more so because I was in awe.

"My dear Levi,

Those sunflowers emulate the warm happiness you bring to my life, the brittle of course your sweetness but also thoughtfulness and endearing humor. I couldn't imagine a better way to have woken up on our day with such a caring and special surprise from you. Thank you for touching my heart in so many unexpected ways. You're my greatest gift this Valentine's."

Life: **Standing Tall**

I'd made a habit of going straight to his section when I walked in the store. I'd spy his frame hunched over a stand and lost in thought. I'd sneak up behind and ask him a question in my best *curious customer* voice. The *it's you* face and nervous jitters that would ensue afterward guilted me a little but bewitched me even more. How could a man so handsome be so humble? Small talk would lead to the invariable question of what I was doing later on, which would then result in a plan. His jitters would wash away into a sunny grin that spread across his whole face, through his arms, right into those nervous fingertips that suddenly found calm. But the happiness started in his deep dark sky-blue eyes, the ones that sparkled of both day and night. It was my turn to have jitters, but those of excitement, for I had plans. With him.

Naturally, I thought of him when we were apart, and I found myself thinking of his frame. The way a person carries themself says a lot about how they feel towards themself inside. I decided I was going to work on that hunch from the inside out. Standing in his kitchen on a sunny afternoon, I told him there was something I wanted to talk to him about. Turning gravely serious, he devoted his full attention to me. "Levi, you have so much to be proud of in yourself. Your strong character. Your sense of respect and appreciation for the world around you. You're handsome. You are a caring person to everyone you meet. Have you ever thought about standing tall? Sometimes, when I see you, you stand low, and I worry you feel low too. I want you to feel as proud of yourself as you deserve and ought to feel. To stand as tall as you are inside."

"Gosh, wow, thank you Allie." He said to the floor, rubbing his neck. Looking up and out the kitchen window he pondered it. "You know, I guess I've never thought about that. Standing tall. I ought to try it. I stand over the shelves all day, and I guess I've got my rib that I don't feel too confident about. It's something I sort of shelter and I'm not proud of."

"Well I have my scar. It's a part of me. It's always going to be. I have the choice to accept it and love it as part of me or reject a part of myself every time I am faced with it. I spent a lot of years feeling absolutely sick inside about it."

"You did? Aw, you shouldn't feel that way about it. It's not bad. Really Allie, you're beautiful. Really you are."

"Well thank you Levi." I smiled back at him. "But I did. And it wasn't until I chose to love my scar as part of me and my journey that it actually healed. And it truly doesn't bother me at all anymore. Sincerely. I don't think *anything* of your rib. Really, I wouldn't know it's there. You do more than anyone." He nodded. "It's a part of you, so I like it." I put my hand there and met his eye with care. He blushed and looked down in that way of his.

"So let's practice." I shifted. Rolling my shoulders back, I modeled for him playfully. He reflected back, glowing, halfway there. I reached over and pulled him higher. "Perfect. That's the man I see." He beamed. The next time I entered the store, I was careful to be sure he didn't see me. I wondered if he'd be standing tall for himself, not for me. He was, and it was my turn to beam.

Life: **Resistance**

As magical as our times were together, our time apart was all the more confusing. The trial prevailed of what seemed to be a lack of space in Levi's life for love, or lack of sustaining desire. He didn't want to change his routines, he didn't want to want, and his resistance was a powerful force. His care for me was apparent, our connection pure, but his priority was clear. Weeks would go by and I wouldn't hear from him, radio silence. Only for him to blow in again, wanting me eagerly. This vacillation was finally enough for me to make a choice. I moved on. Not because I wanted to; because I thought I should. By now, I knew I had to do right by my heart and step off of this ride I was on with him.

Life: Reflection

Reflecting on our time together, I realized that in our time, I'd tried to help him love himself through my eyes. To teach him to love himself through all our late-night talks, a phone call here and there, those messages that I brought to him were life-giving for us both. But I was seeing in him a reflection of me.

The darker side of me I kept silent and didn't burden the world with was my own sharp voice of self-criticism and hardly ceasing thoughts. Oh I carried the burden with me. He was a human example of the consequences of what it did; the hardship it bred. In self-hate and the anxiety of not loving oneself, he made me truly look at myself. What was I doing when I beat myself down every day with inward harshness over little nothings? What did that say about my heart for myself? I needed to listen to my words for him and *feel* I was beautiful too.

I wanted to change inside for someday's sake, for who I wanted myself to be, for the life I wanted to live, and for the love I wanted to be able to receive and to give. In epiphany, I knew I must practice what I'd preached.

It's all a matter of acceptance. Of embracing oneself and shining the light that you have inside. Be your own beacon. We were all meant for a very tender and different purpose. Blessing yourself with loving your gifts is really the only way to share it.

To love thy neighbor, first you must love the most intimate parts of thyself. Never dim your beautiful light. Never deny yourself. You are good enough. You are made perfect. You are who you are for a reason. Learn from yourself. You have gifts. Embrace them. They're here, you're here, to be shared with the world, as it is outside your window.

Reflection: **Resonance**

I believe firmly in the little things in life. I believe it is the little things that make life worth living for those small things really are rather large.

I believe that in love, like life, little things are as large as we make them. The looks, the acts, the presence, the details, are pieces that make a kaleidoscope of color turn in the heart. Do we appreciate the treasures in the little acts of love? Do we drink them in? Appreciation is the seat of tending beauty in our lives.

Alternatively, what blocks love's doorway? Imbalance. How can we know the notes of our song if we play them in our heads without trusting our hearts? Knowing what we want; what we need is a wise, earned gift. Hold onto your knowing. But not too tightly. For when we make believe to ourselves that love has to fit an image of what our life should be, we close ourselves to what it could be. Look within, feel, breathe. Where do we unwittingly limit the universe that delivers in our hearts?

For me, it's trust. Trust in myself, trust in others, trust in life's ultimate process. When we trust life to answer our heart's call, we come to understand that people are attracted to one another the same way we are attracted to a song, to a piece of poetry or art or rhyme. We're drawn to sounds and words which are in unison with where we are in our mind and in our heart. Is this allure not the same with people?

Is it possible that among all the little things we look for in a person, what it really comes down to in finding that true abiding love is something purely intangible, even undefinable? Nuances only spoken by the language in the heart.

Who you are in this present time in life? In fusion with who you have always been. This being that is you in the state that it is sends out a frequency to others that can only be felt beneath the surface. In the subtle tension in the room. In the urges and calls you feel within your spirit telling you to stay, to go, to act, to rest. The deepest.

I know now it's not just practical qualities that bind two people. It's not desire. It's a dimensional, interchanging flow of resonance. Resonance is pure energy. It flows without speaking, touches without touching, finds familiar what it does not know.

When we resonate pain from deep within our souls, we draw a revisiting of that pain out of a subconscious desire to learn from one another, to heal, even if by breaking. With this kind of resonance, we love our partner because they are a reflection of our fractures that need healed; of ourselves that need accepted and held; a reflection of harm that needs overcome. In essence, we are loving the shadow of ourselves in a subconscious effort to shed light upon it. Then, that exchange of each other's teachings of dark, light, and love alchemize the heart into letting go of the past. Again and again until our hearts are ready.

When love doesn't last, it's not loss. It's a coming to the end of a road with a companion who walked with you to teach and learn. Where those paths diverge is the point at which your resonances have shifted, your work with each other achieved, your lessons integrated in your heart. The dimensions of your spirit no longer resonate because this love was for a lesson, not a lifetime. No matter how momentarily heartbreaking in the grand scale of your being, that incompatibility was born from the learning your souls set out to achieve together.

When we resonate love from within, we draw a partner who brings the love we've dreamed of; who's a kindred spirit and a like heart. True love's arrival comes to the resonance of our own holistic self-love. Then, that exalting of light, that exchange of love-lessons, that holding of the dark, it alchemizes the heart into the future.

It's by resonance of the spirit. The soul feels an equality of depth that the mind cannot reason, the heart cannot fully know, and yet we are simply drawn. Drawn by the soul's knowing that we may have found our home.

It seems that people choose a partner that they have the most in common with, that they envision a successful future with by career or by affluence or qualities needed or known. But what so often goes untold in love is a resonance that lies between two people who are meant to be together. Whether for a time or for a lifetime. There is a resonance to be felt between them that cannot be denied. Can you feel it?

Resonance, I believe, lies between what you are and what you need.

The outlying places where you long or you ache, those are the places where you need. They're the resonances you unconscionably send out to someone in a call out for understanding, in life, in yourself, in others you hold dear.

In unison, what you are and what you need act to send out a resonance that calls one to another. Someone feels it, and when they do, your hearts will have spoken before words have a chance to rhyme.

In order to call in the people whom we would like to have in our lives, we must work on our own inner resonance. Ensure that we feel our highest vibration. For if not, we'll deny ourselves our highest match. The fate we deserve in the deepest.

Fate brings together two equals. A pair who resonate to love. But may that pair choose their highest vibration . . . that is the place where resonances become a song.

Life: Albert

Mom's and my feeling of coming home was growing more with each passing trip to our little lake in the north woods. That land called to me inherently, but its people began reaching out and embracing us too. It was the beginnings of more than a home filled with freedom, but also a community full of care. The building of relationships in a world where we were simply us. One day, a formal-seeming gentleman with white hair and calm eyes stopped at our cabin and introduced himself. He'd noticed our presence on the road for quite some time and said that he'd wondered if we were getting our own place. We told him that we didn't have plans to, but still, he invited us for dinner at his home that was up the road over a brook that smelled so earthy I could just sit there and breathe it into my soul. That cool scent both soothed me and woke me up.

Within Albert's inherited home, in the company of his attentive beagle, he was the *host with the most*. Albert introduced Mom and me to the margarita before a thoughtfully planned meal at his long dinner table that took up much of his space. Just as carefully arranged was an assortment of guests at that table, who got to know us, and already knew him. What I saw before me, besides the mashed potatoes, was the kind act he found joy in: bringing people together. I felt the sweet care at how he'd not just noticed us, and welcomed us into his home, but Albert was actually bringing mom and me into the fold of the community. It was his way of better weaving the threads of the community. Over the years, I've come to realize that invitation was one of many he's extended. A welcoming usher of sorts to those who are first stepping foot into this little woodland community.

With every dinner to come that we joined, we slowly felt more a part of the exclusive group that was the lake's summer residents. A collection of people who shared heritage here, like us. Who valued the land and tradition but came from all parts of the country. Snowbirds they were called, unless they were tough enough to live here through its winters and become full-time residents of this land.

A retired caterer for the military, Albert was a man who held an air of formality endearingly blended with humor. Every community needs a man like him. A man who held a strong opinion and a strong heart for maintaining foundations for those around him. He served on the school board. He catered community meals like a well-oiled machine, and it was a fun day working alongside him, just as it was fun letting loose with him. He had a sense of humor that made me imagine the child he used to be someday years ago, making friends with laughs and a hand that reached out, just as it did to us. His friendship and the way his purpose served in our lives was another one of many footsteps to our hearts coming home.

Life: Dave & Christine

Mom and I loved being do-it-yourself women as we sculpted the land on the tiny lot around our small cabin. Together, we laid stone around the foundation, gravel in the driveway, a fence in the yard. No feat was too large for our hands together. We worked well in unison, we flowed quietly. Each of us took joy in working together and watching the fruits of our labors take form as our house turned slowly into a home. That kind of quiet cohesion was one of the essences of our mother-daughter love.

Beside that home of ours was a married couple who vacationed to their cabin on the lake. As I observed these people new to me, it was a quality I noticed was a hallmark of our neighbors' relationship. Each couple has their own kind of love. This was Dave and Christine's. They thrived in supporting one another. They took on projects together, collaborating in the vision, and quietly working in cohesion, creating a work of art by the end. It was amazing what they could do together. And when you watched them, you saw a special love. It was a show of the powerful understanding that flowed between them, that didn't need words, but instead filled in, showed up, shared, predicted, gave space, found roles, held grace.

That love didn't just flow between them. It saw beyond each other.

One day, Mom and I took off a bit more than us do-it-yourself girls could chew. We had a truckload of sod, a sloped hill, a garden hose, and a hot sun. We worked tirelessly, but in truth, we were losing steam and beyond capacity of what we could do this time. Now in my life, reaching out for help was something I didn't know. It simply wasn't in my scope of thought. But help thought of us. Our neighbor walked over and assessed what we were doing. "You girls could use some help. Could I call over a few of my guys in my family here? They could get this done really quickly. My cousin is calling a couple young guys to help. We're gonna get this done." Christine announced.

Guys came by jet ski off the lake, by bicycle from the south, on foot from the north. An uncomfortable amazement at their kindness settled slowly through my bones and I came to fathom a new kind of community. I ran into the house for refreshments as they made quick work of what was breaking our bodies moments ago. I learned what support felt like, the force of a family and the kindness of strangers quickly friends. I learned that neighbors love each other from the well they love their own. And what magnificent neighbors we were blessed to have here today.

As I got to know them, enjoy them, love them, I knew they endured many pains in their lives. More than most. They carried losses that are hard to imagine one family could bear. It makes me wonder how God works hardship in our lives to better serve each other when we allow him more deeply into our hearts. Pains that breed a sense of seeing and compassion that may have enacted that simple, lasting moment between neighbors. They made no effort to hide the fact that they turned to God in their trials. As I do in mine. We are never alone. He is with us when we need Him, and He brings us fellows when we need them too. I learned from Christine and Dave the power of accepting help from those who care to invest in us, and I learned too that a piece of love's art is in peaceful, silent work understood together.

Life: Christian

I first met Christian at a crowded New Year's party the year before. He must have noticed something different about me because that next summer he came to visit me at our cabin. I was shocked and touched. Admittedly, I barely remembered him for the sheer number of people who'd greeted and introduced and come and gone through. When I'd gone sledding with his family, I did remember that he was the man who went airborne down a death trap of a slope with his little dog, Pippa, on his arm. In the sled, Christian flew with a thrilled smile and a laugh that lit up his whole face, while Pippa darted straight to her mama the moment her feet hit the ground. Christian loved life.

With an introspective and analytical mind, he was a vibrant person, filled with a will to live fully. He loved people and enjoyed sharing his passion for living with them. This particular summer, he chose to share that life-love with me.

Our friendship was eclectic, full of humor, sport, and understanding. He'd show up on my doorstep and give me no other choice but minutes to get ready and embark on any number of adventures with a handful of relatives that he'd planned that morning. Be it tennis, four-wheeling, breakfast, or bikes, simple things sparked big inspiration to laugh and connect and learn.

A part of him seemed lonely and needing of shared meaning. With curiosity, he sought to learn from me the histories of the many people on our lake I'd quickly become connected to. With an encouraging eye, Christian sought to teach me tennis and maybe even spontaneity. We shared as many laughs as we did substantive conversations. It was a friendship that recognized we held equal measures of depth and maybe unequal measures of loosen-up. Through Christian, I realized I needed to *live*. He inspired me to "Get out and do it!" through the rest of my life.

In my dream after his sudden passing on an ocean beach, Christian played the song, *Live Like You Were Dying* and told me that he was going to have fun watching my life play out. An old man and a young girl, I was sure God placed us together in all our uncommon connectedness. It seems to me that the most unexpected of friends are most often God's handiwork in motion. People brought together to share in the building of each other's spirits.

Reflection: Sunflower

A sunflower. A simple sunflower rising from the earth greets the sun. It says hello, and it lingers there. From the perspective of the sun shining back at it, the flower's face remains there until the dusk calls night to end the day. Whenceforth the sunflower waits. For when it's fellow rises again, it will follow. Two faces, mirroring each other in jubilee. Shining in salutation that is steady, ever reaching, always present. For the sun always rises, and the flower always shines its face right back into it. As if, each of their own right, they're sharing a common energy, the mind that illuminates, stores up, and then shares a glory with the world.

When we find our sun, following it comes as naturally and rhythmically as this flower. It's woven into the fiber of our being. It's following our inner light that's a part of a greater source, that's shared with everyone, but sometimes especially someone. When we follow our sun, we're greeting a glorious part of our soul. The kind that always lights the day and awaits through the night faithfully.

Life: The Guys and Girls

Beyond the several years of friendship built between us, the relationships Mom and I had forged with Jack's friends, Henry and Cecilia, Carlton and Maria, and Lawrence, deepened for years beyond Jack's passing. Built upon an instantaneous connection, those bonds remained over memories and meaning shared. Sometimes, a simple memory poignantly displays the shape of a friendship. Of the cache of times shared between us and "the guys and girls," I hold fondly a particular misty spring morning.

I had just finished a long visit with Christian, who'd popped in as he always did. I was bustling around the house, when I started at a knock at the door. It was Carlton! The moment I opened the door, his shy face spread into a sincere smile. "You want to go for a ride with Henry and I while the girls are out doing laundry?"

Excitement and honor coursed through my veins at their thoughtfulness and the spontaneous opportunity to be with them. "Of course! Thank you for inviting me! I'll get ready real quick."

"You take your time." He said genuinely, turning to go.

I dressed in all my warm layers and ran to their rental cabins. Maria's machine was waiting for me. They showed me how to use the controls since I'd always used Jack's in the past, a flicker of absence I knew we were all conscious of.

The trails were wet but beautiful. I found myself humming as we rode, knowing no one could hear if I did. We saw a group of four deer, each of us appreciating them just the same. It was refreshing being deep in the woods, invigorating charting new terrain, adventurous in a way that thrilled me. But most of all, I loved riding with the guys. Henry in front, Carlton in the back, a sheltering team as if I were precious cargo. We rode all the way up to the highest point in the region, Mt. Baldy. It was something I knew the girls would never have been game for, but I loved every second of the rough and tricky terrain, like life on the edge. The ride up was filled with tall trees and earthy scents, and the breeze of our speed.

At the base of Mt. Baldy, Henry got off. "Now there's gonna be some roots in the trail and we'll be going uphill and downhill. You go as fast or slow as you're comfortable going. Don't feel like you have to keep up with me. I'll be ahead of you on the trail just a ways either way. You just go as fast as you feel comfortable and be sure to look around and take it in. It's got some real good views." My heart felt loved.

These two people, likely so simple on the surface to most they met, gave me some of the most profound kind of mutual seeing and tending kind of friendship. The kind that fell out of the clear blue sky, which goes to show, God gives us what we need most, we don't even have to search. Our job is to just treasure them and take them in for all they're worth. That's exactly what I was doing right now.

When we came down from Mt. Baldy, we stopped, and they offered to go home, being mindful of how much I did or didn't want to do. I said I was up for more. They exchanged a look loaded with all the feelings they'd pent up. With me, they'd be able to express they were still young enough to go that far. They could go all the places their wives wouldn't dare nor would they for the sake of their fussing. In their hope to give me a good adventure, they were regaining a sense of their own they longed for. It's funny how friendships work in that fashion, symbiotically in the smallest of ways.

Again, Henry prepared me for what to expect on our next stretch. "We're gonna go on the Perimeter Trail. There'll be a canopy of branches you may have to duck or swing out of the way. Then, we'll end up on the north end of the club." And boy was there ever! I found myself ducking and bowing all the way through.

When we returned, we stood beside our machines and chatted about the ride and this and that. The girls returned from their laundry duties. "Haven't you got sense enough to get out of the rain?" Cecilia asked, smiling in amusement. We hadn't really noticed the mist. Conversation was too good.

"We rode up Mt. Baldy, the Perimeter Trail, N Trail, and B Trail. Totaled 24 miles." Both men shared a youthful glimmer in their eyes as they exchanged a look beyond Cecilia and Maria's gasps. I smiled behind my sunglasses, that glimmer sparkling inside next to the memory I had made here today with them. I took a snapshot of this moment in my mind's eye before I moseyed on home and got warmed up with a shower.

Our friendship with Henry, Cecilia, Carlton, and Maria was uniquely and inherently true. We spoke openly, shared common thoughts, enjoyed each other. We'd share a pizza and an evening and unfold each other's best memories as we made new ones together. Talking about how the couples met, farming, Jack, school back in the day, and family. We got to hear of their adventures snowmobiling together, sometimes with as many as 32 people, but most often with Cecilia being a bit of a rambunctious driver. As they teased her, she'd playfully cover her face with a twinkle in her eye. I loved taking in their playfulness that fell so naturally with sentiment.

In kind, I playfully told the guys they should feel special; that I'm going to break a date for them. That I wouldn't miss out on time together with them for a guy. Henry smiled real big. They couldn't believe it. Carlton said, "Well you can just tell him that you have family up here and this is their last day and you'd like to spend it with them."

With a short nod, Henry added, "That's true."

I smiled back, "That IS the truth. You guys all are family." The best thing about friends, I've learned, is that they are a family you've hand-chosen by a love that calls from your heart and theirs.

Life: **Perspectives**

Back in Illinois, I was chasing a different kind of dream than freedom. The greatest dream in my life was to find love. Not just lasting love, but the kind that filled and flowed between the depths of two hearts and minds and souls. I wanted the man that I had felt in my heart since I first understood what love was. That made this search for him undefinable yet so very clear. It was like I could feel the many nuances of him, and with every suitor I quickly knew my search must continue.

Sometimes I felt an ache of longing for this person so known yet unseen that I was afraid I would never find him. Deep down, I hoped that if I just searched harder, gained more experience, that the love I longed for would appear in my life. I was dating seven men at one point, each of them with their own blend of qualities. I thought back to a memory with my father.

This evening, I was going out with my friend, Luke. I playfully called him Lucky. He was a sweet guy with a great family, and we had a lot of fun when we were together. My mother loved him, but I knew he wasn't right for me. Not in that capacity. And even though he knew that, he still wanted to be friends. I was still his wedding date and fellow movie-goer. We just kept things pure and simple. We had fun together and did meaningful things. It was light yet heartfelt, which was just what we needed. He was who I had a date with tonight.

"I won't be home for dinner tonight. I'm going out with a friend. But I heated up some roast and potatoes with carrots for you. It's on the table." I said to Dad as he waited at the dinner table with his evening paper.

"Is this friend a date?" he asked with a tinge of judgement.

"I guess you could call it that. Well, yes it is. Why?"

"It must be nice to be liked." He chewed his food pensively. "Which one is it tonight?" he mused somewhat cynically, though his humor always had that air to it.

I told him, but he didn't seem to recall his name. I reminded him of when he had met the man. Still no recollection. It didn't make much difference to me. I knew to fend for myself when it came to dating.

"You know you seem to find a problem with most of the men you date." he continued.

"It's not that I find something wrong. It's that I'm not going to settle. I know what I want and what I don't want, and there's nothing wrong with that. I'm not going to waste my time, my feelings, or theirs when I know it's not right." Most of the time, I didn't let him ruffle my feathers, but in this matter, I had to stand in my convictions and speak up for myself. I was no wounded bird evading love. I was in fact the opposite. I chose the courageous road of being strong enough to wait. Have enough self-worth to wait. A value I'd earned from experience.

"Well one of these days, you're going to have to just pick one." He sat down his fork on the table and looked at me.

"Pick one." I echoed flatly. He didn't know what love is, never had.

"You just make it work. That's what marriage is." I stood there in silence, keys in hand, knowing all the words I wanted to say but also that they would bring nothing productive to his rigid ideals. That too, I'd learned from experience. So I simply sighed and excused myself for a night of fun. I can't deny that words like that didn't hurt me. I wished my dad wanted more for me. But it seemed he couldn't conceptualize it even for himself, and he'd wanted far less for me before. I learned from times with my father that it's important to be truthful with ourselves about how others think and feel based on their actions and their words, and even based on our instincts. There's solidarity in that.

In that fervent search for my partner in life, I found more disappointment and disillusionment that waned my hope. Finally, I stopped searching and decided to build into my own life and heart. What I learned from that season was that sometimes you can't chase a dream; you have to have the patience it takes for that dream to come. I decided that I needed to foster my heart for this kind of love, and I trusted that God would send him when I was ready.

Life: **Loving with Limits**

I came into the store with Mom. It had been many months of no contact with Levi. We were through. I was strong in it, or so I said. When I told Mom I would go get the lettuce, I saw a look of question in her eyes. Maybe concern. I wasn't afraid to be close to him. I think I was challenging myself, finally ready for it. Ready to be aloof. Who was I kidding? I knew exactly what I was doing.

"Hey Allie." I heard his friendly voice beside me. He was jittery with nerves today. But he stood tall. My mind went to his kitchen for a moment.

"Hello Levi." I replied rather coolly. Right on point. Don't pretend it's forgotten.

"How are you doing? How's your mom? I see her come in the store now and then."

"She's fine. Been staying busy. Your parents been well?" I could feel my desperate feelings seeping in my heart. Wanting us so. Ugh.

"Good, good. We still walk the dogs. How about you Allie. How are you?" He was so pointed and serious in asking. He didn't meet my eye, but he was gazing at the shredded carrots like they could have scripture encrypted in them. The question held meaning.

"I've been okay. Keeping busy with school." I didn't really know what to say.

"Oh yeah? So nothing really much has changed? Anything new going on with you?" He met my eyes for a moment with an openness now. Hope.

"No, nothing new." Was he inquiring if there was anyone in my life? It felt that way when relief washed over his shoulders.

"Well Allie, it was good to see you. Really it was." He paused a moment. "I don't know. Maybe you'd want to see each other, go for a walk tonight?"

"Sure. I'd like that." I know some disciplinarian part of me that was shaking her head at me and tapping her foot. Tsking at the choices I was foolishly making with my heart all over again. But I didn't care. I floated away from the stand of lemons feeling rather yellow. Yellow is a happy color they say. Maybe it was the smile on his face that slid right into mine.

Life: The Walk

As we walked down chilly side streets, he was nervous again like old times. But he had a fresh air about him, and at least he talked.

He spoke of all the things I'd planted in his heart and his life. Described how he'd changed the way he was living and being from the inside out. I could see truth in his words too. Life. Yet in all those words, he never connected with me. He was simply stating facts nervously, as if proving that he didn't need me anymore. And yet he'd gaze out across the field and then intently into my eyes with a scared and desperate plea inside them. I always soothed those eyes, and he always poured out from himself when I did. It was the push-pull that was so classic for us. In that moment, I could see it all so clearly that it hurt. But more than hurt, it exasperated me. Was this healthy love? Was this what I wanted for the rest of my life? Someone who needed me to reach through to him; to rebuild him. Someone with whom sharing love was only possible if I facilitated its release? Within him and between us? Suddenly, as I stared across the table, I saw how imbalanced and even toxic our relationship was. I needed different; more. I needed to stop.

So, instead of reaching in and teasing out that beautiful heart and its love for me, instead of answering the plea of those wide desperate eyes to release him from himself, I stood. The air between us filled even more with anxious tension.

"Levi, thank you for letting me in. I realize that you let very few people into your circle, and I feel honored to be a part of it. To have your trust. You're an exceptional man with so much depth, care for others, everything really. You see the meaning in every day, and you treat everyone in this world with so much respect. I'm lucky to get to see that. To know you in this way. I know you like to keep to yourself, and allowing me into your world had to be a step outside your comfort zone. Thank you for choosing to allow me in. Your friendship is a true gift." Saying these things to him gave me peace in knowing that he heard them. I decided it was time to move on. But not to someone else. It was time I practice what I preached to him. It was time I loved myself.

He held me and kissed me one last time as I left. This time, he didn't sweep me away. I wasn't lost in the moment with nothing else but him. The touch of his fingers didn't electrify my skin and the feel of his lips were just a kiss. His arms held a firm embrace but lacked the strength of the meaning they once pressed into my frame. And as I drove away, this time I didn't cry. I just felt hollow inside.

When I got home later that night, I was stoic through the evening until something about my shower let my feelings run too. I walked into my mother's room, and I sobbed. I sobbed for all the love I had for him that I needed to give up. Just like times before. I sobbed for the beautiful person inside him that I wanted so badly for the world to see, for him to see. I wanted him to value and care for himself every day the way I did, the way I had tried so unwaveringly to show him. If only he could reach in beyond the mean inner voices and feelings that muted his light. I sobbed for what could have been even though I knew that dream wasn't reality. I cried for the friend I lost who saw my spirit, never looking at me in a shallow way. He listened to me with his heart and he loved me with his spirit. It was his mind that I could never find home in. I knew he let go of our love, and I also knew why. He couldn't be steady or consistent or reliable. I had to accept the fact that I deserved more, regardless of what I thought I wanted. I knew I could do that for myself.

Levi taught me what chemistry felt like. I'm not talking sexual attraction. This is pure magic, get caught up in it, nothing else in the world chemistry. The kind that electrifies your being when his fingertips touch your skin as he tenderly rubs your arm to and fro as the quiet evening turns to night. Knowing there was someone, somewhere who felt deep like me, who loved from the spirit with me, made me feel a little more at home in it.

Levi and I were kindred yet very different. With what we lacked, I learned love must be given and received, mind, body, and soul. I was ever grateful for that lesson. I loved him for his friendship and for the way he made me feel. He'd taught me to trust a little again, even though he broke my heart. By loving him into a stronger man, I found reflected back to me a shadow of myself that needed light.

I learned with Levi that you must love yourself to be loved; that the amount of love you're willing to give yourself is the very amount of love you are ready to receive from those around you, be it a partner or a friend, even a passerby. How much you love yourself even affects how you receive the world and how the world receives you. Without one partner knowing their worth, you so often can't fully, truly have the other. I knew I had a lot of work to do.

While I treasured Levi, I knew that I had to let go of my "broken winged birds." Their broken parts were not mine to heal, and my love was not going to change them. I had to live in the truth that people have to choose to heal themselves, to love themselves, and only they can do it.

Levi taught me what real love feels like . . . in semblances. Because a part of me knew that there was still so much more, and though I hadn't found it yet, in my soul I remembered what true love was like.

I knew that what we'd shared with one another was like a sea ship in a bottle. Beautifully setting sail under a gentle sky and on a breathless breeze. But its magic and its wisdom was bottled. Touch it and you feel it again. Shake it and you know in each direction the voyage had an inevitable end of translucent, impermeable glass.

All these memories and lessons of us I kept in that bottle, and they grew in my heart. All the while I was teaching him self-worth, I was teaching myself too. There's beauty in God's design that way. I believe that sometimes God collaborates some of his greatest works with us while shining the light on our feet.

Reflection: Swallowtail

A swallowtail struggled into view, showing me the cadence of its droughting efforts. I leapt to the ground as my heart followed. Stepping swiftly onto my hand, I saw a soul in need with a single broken wing. Quickly enveloped in my sheltering hand, he was now protected from the forceful wind. His struggling ceased. Seeing the relief wash over him touched me, to know his world was better, easier. I could feel the spark in his heart next to the tired weariness in his spirit. I embraced him with all my love in hopes he could feel it.

My thoughts became absorbed in protecting him from harm, fixing that wing, wanting so much for him to fly again so he could be well and free. I lost all sense of myself and what I'd been doing. There was only this little creature whom I wanted so deeply to help. I searched for ways to fix this for him. I thought about placing him on my hummingbird feeder, but it would make him vulnerable to birds. I considered a flower for shelter from the wind.

Sadness settled in my heart. I had to accept the truth that I couldn't make him fly again. What was in my hands was the simple ability to make his time in this world better, easier, more loved. Beyond that, I had to let go.

In some cases, an outside force can come in and cast a rainbow of change upon a cloudy sky. But the greatest power for healing in one's life rests within their own spirit and soul. Because the challenges we face in life are our own. They're ours to face, and ours to take. When we heal them within ourselves, we empower a spirit of evolution within our soul that no other can ignite nor perpetuate. Real change.

If we were to change and evolve on behalf of other's souls, we would deny them the feeling of earning their wings to fly on their own, in this life or beyond. They could never know what it means to deepen their faith through struggle, triumph over trial. Just as importantly, everyone deserves the fulfillment and independence that come with healing thyself. It is through facing our most harrowing trials and hollowing truths, alone or beside someone, that we become strong of mind and heart and mature of spirit and soul. It's a process of living that one can only give to oneself. True change and growth can only happen by the will of self; it's a law of existence.

I'd tended and mended many swallowtails in my life, perhaps every one that'd crossed my path. They clung to the tenderness and joy I poured onto them just as this butterfly on our walk together, finding shelter and love in their storm. To be their haven made me feel worthy in this world, and it gave me value for myself. Until I learned to let them go and not be everything to everyone. I learned to give to myself instead of pouring into cracked vases.

It took me years and countless "projects" to appreciate the power of personal ownership for healing to truly transpire. Once I understood that, I knew how to empower and free not just my butterflies, but myself. Because no longer did I endow myself to be their savior. I had to believe I wasn't responsible for the well-being of the world, or even of my world. In matters of the heart and soul, sometimes only we can save ourselves. I learned to focus more on the me I'd come to dismiss; to notice how I felt and learn how to care for me.

By being strong in myself, I knew that instead of healing others, I could lend a helping hand, be a guiding light. I found the strength to care but did not carry. And in doing so, I learned how to honor others' trials and also honor myself.

As I let go of my need to fix this swallowtail butterfly in my hand, I allowed acceptance and thanked him. Holding him helped me understand that even though I can't heal the world around me, my love is more than enough.

The Valleys Fuel the Peaks

Life has a way of testing our wings. Every life is filled with high points and low points. In every trial lies an opportunity to draw closer to God and to who we are, or the choice to stray away from that.

It gives us opportunities to heal ourselves through our trials based on the choices we make in the face of them. We may deny ourselves growth of healing and inadvertently choose sorrow or remorse, resentment or hate, envy or listlessness wherein we lose ourselves. Or we can lean into God. We can reach up for His healing hand and let Him walk beside us through our struggle until we've become a new measure of strong and wise. I believe God rests within every soul. I believe that His will is ours to know if we seek Him. I believe these things because that's the path I chose.

Within every soul lies the will to persist and the potential to overcome by hope, faith, love, acceptance, truth. But not in an airy sense that goes undirected and undefined. We must seek our soul and silence the noise, both outside and within, to hear what our heart and soul is guiding us to. I believe that inner knowing is like God's voice and yours speaking in cohesion to guide your way. You'll know it too because it's always a voice of Love. Stay ever in touch with this voice.

Consult this voice when you have wings that need mended. You'll still fall into the valleys in life. They're a part of living. But after you fallen, you'll see that the valley's breakdown and despair helped you see all the truths you needed in order to appreciate the view when you climbed to the peaks.

When the valleys of those broken swallowtail wings ache, when they feel like they'll never end, keep the faith. Faith is all that will keep you to the end. It's what will connect you to that abiding voice within that keeps you going, keeps you on the path to your own glory. Your light that shines ever-brightly. It is not dim, if only you can see it, hear it, know it is always there. With every healing wingbeat, you are growing. And when you fly, the pigments of every color in your wings will hold a depth of color that matches the new understandings built into your spirit from your pathway. Colors of compassion, empowerment, peace, understanding, a higher kind of love.

Sometimes, I think we underestimate the valleys in our lives. They tear our hearts out. Test the limits of our psyches, our resolve, bring to surface old forgotten wounds. But it's these valleys, these times in which we are tried in the most frightening and gut wrenching of ways that we have the greatest opportunity to deepen our faith. Each time I've met these trials, I've been affirmed an existing truth. One that pervades my very existence: The valleys fuel the peaks.

Life: The Landscapes of our Lives

As I grew into a woman, I came to feel like every part of who I was was someone my father outright did not like. He hid others' compliments for me, dug at my confidence and criticized every high achievement, save for those he chose to simply ignore altogether with pointed nonchalance. He used my kindness until he was through with me and then he swiftly cast me aside with hate. I remember every sting. I can still feel every current of hate when I think back on it. I can see those eyes searing into me. Every ounce of it struck into my core. Layers of pain amidst layers of love. Just like the rings on a tree, these were my memories.

It took me a long time to realize it, but I learned that people show you exactly who they are. It's up to you to hear it, see it, know it. It's up to you to make the choice to accept the truth that people demonstrate to you rather than a prettier lie you want to believe. In that acceptance lies great power to have faith in your judgement and be firm in your way.

After every talk and moment we had, my father and I were both faced with choices. I empowered him. I gave him the option to choose love, and he made it very clear he was making a choice, every morning, every evening, each weekend, each moment with us. His choice was complexly simple. My acts of patience and grace in teaching him love gave me peace in knowing I was doing everything I could, but they still showed me the truth I was left to face.

Incomprehensible as it seemed to me, he didn't want my love, and he didn't want me. Larger than that, he didn't want to feel good. Resentment was a choice he entered into every day. Holding control over others and manipulating them to his advantage was how he related to and felt rooting in the world. Seeing these things left me with the challenging choice to accept the truth of him. No matter what I saw, no matter what I felt, I couldn't choose for him to love. Any more than I could choose for my mother to leave.

Although Dad had told me very plainly his philosophy on life and his choice to play a certain role in it, for years I couldn't help but ignore plain truths and try harder. Sometimes the truth hurts, sometimes it doesn't fit with the ideas we want to hope for. So we keep on hoping anyway. We hold on and fight for a change. We persist with willful hope. We resist accepting.

No matter how much that willful hope eases the pain of the truth in the short term, when we don't accept hard truths, we cause ourselves larger, deeper pain. In reality, we're denying ourselves peace. That resistance takes up space in our lives where living could be. It creates a push and pull and a high and low, whereas truth's peace could bring more goodness into our lives. Sometimes, letting go of what we wish and accepting what is empowers a strength and faith in oneself. Acceptance of truth frees you from false narratives and allows the grace to let yourself let go.

I took so much responsibility onto my shoulders because I couldn't accept the way things were. I made the mistake of believing that I could change circumstances out of my control with the power of love. Love is immeasurably transformational, but I couldn't love truths away. My dad wasn't balanced. He wasn't able to love me the way I wanted to share it with him. My mom wasn't ready to leave him. No amount of unconditional love was going to change their psychology. But what it did do was chip away at my sense of being loved myself. It eroded my sense of welfare and even my faith in myself. I did that to me because I couldn't accept the truth.

Learning acceptance the hard way became a lesson God showed me again and again, not just through my dad, but through deep and pivotal heartbreaks of my life. I believe it's through these heartbreaks I learned how to listen to God and to myself. I realized the value in recognizing His signs, His stirrings, and my knowings. I discovered that, through all of it, God and I were sculpting me into a stronger woman, redefining what strength really means. And as I reached for God from my deepest valleys, I felt His presence with me. He drew close to me and through evolving through these challenges, I learned how the valleys fuel the peaks.

Reflection: Dream Catcher

The great blue heron stands upon the poles of his legs, a pillar in the water gazing upon a blackened slate of glass. The stillness of the night allows a peace to settle into his feathers, upon his mind. And the water, void of its color of day, makes it a canvas for the stars, a reflection not unlike the sky above.

The heron stands in the stillness of the morning water, just before the dawning sun lights the day. He gazes down at the reflection of the sky above, searching for his fish. Instead, all he sees is a blackened void filled with stars. Twinkling in the ripples of his footsteps. As if he could move their transits through the blanketed sky. At once, a dream catches him. He looks up. Which is the true reflection? The romance of his first sighting or the reality of what he's reaching for as his feathers take him ever higher towards them? He may not know. But what he sees is that he was inspired to fly at a time when he looked for fish and found only darkness. He is a star catcher because he is a dream follower. Cannot any one of us be him if we believe?

Life: We're All Dreamers

I believe we must follow the dreams that lodge themselves into our hearts. If we don't, an integral part of our life goes unfulfilled, a mission undone. When we deny ourselves our dreams, we earn ourselves regrets. We feel life incomplete. We wonder in a way that's filled with the shadows of doubt and knots of regret.

I don't want to look back with that kind of wonder. I endeavor to chase my every dream because I acknowledge each one as something greater than myself. I believe God plants dreams in our spirit, a calling, a stirring of where we belong, what we're meant to do. I believe that when we say yes to these things, no matter how outlandish they may seem, God conspires to help us achieve them. After all, dreams and passions are planted in every heart and soul for a reason. Because *you* can grow them into something beautiful.

Life: Dream Casting

I looked out the window onto the lake and a familiar knowing settled into my bones. It tapped on the shoulder of my spirit. *This is your home.* I know it is. It always has been.

As I did many years when the end of summer came, I toyed with the idea of getting a job here, setting up life only for reality to set in, that the circumstances I'd left behind at summer's start held those plans back. But still, it never quieted that yearning plea inside of me to come home to stay.

My eyes drew up to the stilling sky as they'd done so many times. The same sky that set a spark of hope and faith inside me. I felt as definitive as a bell's ring, God telling me *Not yet. There were things I needed to do first. But soon.* I could have this if I grew toward it. Resolutely, I turned to my mother and shared with her my dream for home here.

A dream becomes a reality with faith and a spirit to achieve it. We all have inside of us dreams waiting to be actualized. Some dreams we don't even realize we have until they're placed into our laps and filling our hearts in ways we'd never known before. Dreams aren't just for believers. Dreams make believers. The same goes for faith.

In the months that followed my gaze out the window, I spent a lot of time doing my part. I felt God urging me to learn a lesson that I'd had coming for years: *Be content with where you are, happy living anywhere.* So, I found joy in the small things: the local park, a new coffee shop downtown, the way the birds rang in the spring, the shine of our brick road after it rained in an early morning streetlight run. By learning this value, I felt like I was able to come to a loving peace with what was and a graceful place of letting go of what was not. Only then did I understand what a gift that lesson was. And the corner of my heart that held home deepened over that time.

For years, I'd lived for summers, lived for time spent away from the place I called home. I lived for the summers because in my summer world, I tasted the freedom to feel and think and be myself in a way that ignited my flame for living. It did for both of us, my best friend and me.

What else God was nudging me to do was to breach beyond the safety of my well-oiled techniques of patient cordiality or invisibility and instead meet my father's extremes with nothing but calm and loving compassion. The unconditional kind that quietly, sincerely endures all and does its best to understand all. In doing so, change ensued.

Reflection: The Storm

Ripples of change come like the clouds with the weather.

A storm is coming. Listen. Act. Feel its energy course through you. It has something to tell you about your life. It will destruct. When it leaves, things will be broken and damaged you never thought would be. But as you sort the debris, you'll find those ripples cast an effect that reaches far and wide, reshaping and sculpting your present in a way that feels strange and casts your future in a new lens you've yet to fully hold. But let me tell you, the energy of that storm should not be feared. It is the very storm that makes anew. Honor the old, but look onward. Beautiful color touches the horizon if only we choose to see.

When it storms up here it feels as though the sky is closer than anywhere else on Earth. You feel it in your bones as a boom of thunder reverberates through your chest, clashes right over the cabin, echoes through the treetops. Is it possible that the sky could really be that close? That this thunder could crack just above your rooftop? You'll wonder until you're drawn to the window against your mother's will to see the piercing electric fingers of lightning stretch across the sky. Only for a moment. Leaving you lingering in awe at the pane holding your breath for one more rumble through your rib cage. It's like all that electricity charges the air and channels right through my spirit. I could think of no better way to start the day.

The lake quivers with raindrops. Rain pelts the window in drops that seemed to get larger by the moment, making this cabin I adore feel like a cozy haven. A small part of me, okay a big part of me, hoped the power would go out just so we could get out the lanterns and light the candles, nothing else but that warm glow. I went around the house and lit them, just to capture that feeling. And I just sat and took it in. Just like that, it was gone as quickly as it came. The hush of gentle rain chasing in its wake.

Life: Idea

Now autumn, I'd been reflecting on God's vast stirrings in my heart. Mom had spent most of her life taking care of others. It was time that she took care of herself and spent some time in our special place, just for her. I proposed the idea that she go. I knew it would be liberating to her. And I assured her that I had work. I could take care of the home. What I didn't say was that, beneath it all, I wanted her to feel free, joyful, at peace, in all the ways she could feel, up there in our cabin in the north woods. To my glee, she said yes.

In my weeks home alone with Dad, I felt God continue to stir my heart. It was like God was urging me that I needed to learn to love my hometown in order to find a home in my north woods. I needed to find the things I loved about it and accept it, not reject it altogether as I had come to feel. At first, I thought it odd, but the more I rested in His message, I realized it was a strong lesson to be happy where you're at and embrace your roots. To love where we come from, no matter what's been, is a powerful thing. So, I got out a whole lot more. I took evening walks at sunset at my favorite park, and I discovered places in that park I had never seen that were *beautiful.* I walked neighborhoods, exploring. I went on dates and had *fun.* I visited our local coffee shop for the first time. I *loved it.* That shop became my haven at times when Dad was intense. I think when we live in intense homes or workplaces, even times, we all need a haven at our fingertips. It can bring us back to center.

But I also had a hope. Years ago, in my teens, I'd realized that life with Dad was easier when I chose not to look, to speak to Dad as little as I could, to be unseen. To be unseen was to be unknown, and to be unknown was to be safe. With just the two of us in the home now, I laid that all aside. Perhaps I could show him that, no matter what, he was unconditionally loved. That no matter what he said or did, I would be steady and calm and loving him. So, I did.

With just the two of us, Dad had been a little unhinged. He would get angry at me for wearing color when I ran, meeting me at the door and reminding me that I was just asking to be raped and killed and left at the side of the road; that I was asking for it. It unnerved me, the energy behind his words, but I didn't bend to them. I never had. An air of domination loomed overhead, and I couldn't tell if he was trying to provoke conflict or just releasing raw energy over losing his semblances of control. Regardless of the reason, I felt unsettled, disturbed, unsure of where he and I were headed. Sometimes, I found reprieve sitting by the cabinets in the bathroom, where the door locked and I could hear the birds outside the window. He knew how to mirror people, and I don't know if he even knew he was doing it. Sometimes, he seemed to mirror all the things I was interested in. I wanted to draw in, to feel it, but I had to resist in spite of my heart. I knew that this was what happened when I let him really know me and see me. I had been wise enough to protect such things through the years, but I'd given that safety up when I saw hope for giving him faith in God. I knowingly sacrificed my security for the chance he could find God. Deep down I hoped it would heal him because in finding God, he'd find Love.

The hard truths I hadn't accepted yet was that, whether he found God or not, his psychology wouldn't change. The same dynamics would exist between he and I. And with the vulnerability I had shown to him, I would never really be able to tell if he were mirroring me or loving me. I was susceptible to manipulation if I stayed as close as I had come these past few weeks. I didn't want that to be the truth, though. I wanted the truth to be that our relationship was healed, closer, seen, felt, and understood. That grace and forgiveness could bring out the kind of companionship I wished were possible. Sometimes to ignore the truth is to choose to be naive. Being naive feels better sometimes.

I hadn't fully accepted yet that to love someone doesn't always mean you can invite them into your inner spaces. To love doesn't always mean it's safe to be close. Truth is, sometimes, to love ourselves, we must love others from a distance.

Life: Chaos

It was evening, and Dad was home from work, ruminating. After hearing a few more slams and huffs than usual for this time of night from him, I hopped off the couch and walked swiftly to the bottom of the stairs asking Dad what was wrong.

He was standing at the top of the stairs, intensified from alcohol. I could see it in his posture. "Oh, I'm just pissed off. Nothing you don't already probably know. It's not about you. It's your mother and I. And it's not because I've had too much to drink either." Funny he recognized that.

I knew how to dance the careful steps so as to not stir his hatred. I danced them so well that it'd been years since I'd seen the black in his eyes toward me, though I remembered the feel of his hate as if it were moments ago. I'd figured out how to quiet that piece inside him. "I didn't realize you had something to drink. Are you okay?" My voice stayed even, friendly, concerned, not showing I saw any more than I let on.

"So what?" his tone suddenly cutting, assertive. He was looking for a confrontation to get high on. It didn't just please him. It fueled him, enlivened his spirit. "You think I'm *drunk*? Is my *speech* slurring? *Am* I staggering? You'd *know* if I was *drunk*." Legs spread apart, holding a towel at the top of the stairs, daring me. I'd never seen him fully drunk before. I knew he'd been stopping at the store every night after work. Four beers, a bottle of wine, brandy mixed with juice, had become his go-tos. He found pleasure in his buzz before dinner. It was a controlled addiction Mom and I had quietly monitored through the years as it ebbed and flowed, greeting the bottle first upon his arrivals home from work each night. Lately, dinner had gotten smaller and smaller to feel the high more, which he proudly admitted to me. I suppose my naivete of it had kept me from fully acknowledging how much he'd been spiraling these past few weeks.

"I'm only asking because you said something about it. I never would have known you had anything to drink." Keeping my voice calm and nonreactive was key, but I was also able to keep myself calm rather than being emotional from years of practice. It was a skill that transgressed to all facets of my life whether I liked it or not. Sometimes I wondered, Is that part of who I am or did I become that? I wasn't sure. At times I wished I could just feel things in the moment, not later when I was alone and safe. But it was a gift, too, that I was grateful for. It allowed me to be strong for those I love, be cool under pressure, and think in emergencies. It's made me ready for life in countless ways that empower me and soothe and stabilize others. Innate or learned, I wouldn't trade it.

After too much back and forth between us, I gently calmed him from his angry place of rumination and aggression. I'd sincerely wanted to help him sort through his feelings and make it better, but I'd grown tired of how he'd want me to cajole for him to share his feelings. I returned to the living room.

I took a breath and resumed writing in my notebook in my own space. In short time, though, he came to me. He sat down in his chair and waited for me to ask again. Deep in scribing my thoughts, I finished getting them down. As he angrily stood to leave the room, I asked him if he wanted to talk to me. I couldn't let him leave that way. He clearly needed to get something out.

He inched a few thoughts out, first with calculated looks at the wall, thoughtfully placed words, and then less and less filter until he was spewing them out without reason or regard and frankly much sense. Things like, "I was never a family man anyway. I should never have gotten married." I listened and replied as his filter fell entirely away and his aggression returned. I had not seen this side of his personality in full form in years, yet I fell skillfully back in step, maneuvering the blunt and spiteful conversation. To my shock, it all amounted to the fact that my father wanted to leave my mom. Not just that, but I thought he disliked her in the same way that he used to resent me not so many years ago. That scared me for her. I knew what that felt like.

Life: Flashback

I still remember one day coming home a couple hours late from out of town. My parents' conversation had gone like this.

"She's not home yet." Dad sat at our breakfast nook table, eyes intently calculating the odds as he cast his sights across the road.

"She's probably visiting. She said she might be longer," Mom replied, bringing logic into the conversations.

"Maybe she was in an accident," he suggested, casually.

"No. If that were the case, we would have gotten a call from the police," she asserted.

"Maybe she died in a fiery car crash, burned beyond recognition. No license, not even dental records. We wouldn't get a call."

Life: Bedtime

Having shared his thoughts, Dad went upstairs. After he'd gone to bed, my mind could not turn off. Was Mom safe around Dad with him feeling so much resentment towards her not idolizing him? Would his statements hold true in the morning, freeing us? Dare I believe that? Or were they simply the ramblings of his ale? Would Mom be open to this idea, to allowing this change? What would happen? So many questions.

A quiet part of me felt sadness at what was happening. I thought I would feel elated. After all my lifetime of spending years in a home where happy moments seen were squelched by the chagrin of someone else, I thought that this newfound liberty would be an exuberant release. I'd dreamed of this freedom more times than I could count. In more ways than one would imagine, but somehow, I'd never imagined this.

Life: Open Door

The next morning, I felt sick. A steak knife slid down my throat each time I swallowed, making me rear back in pain. I barely felt up for leaving the couch, let alone working on my projects. Piece by piece, I'd been creating the beautiful quilt that was an outlet of passion and love and beauty in the face of the watching, the baiting, the death fantasies and threats, fear projections, attempts at control, in all the abuse I was enduring. Quilting for me took me somewhere out of my mind and into a place of peace. We all need those outlets, I believe. However, I had plenty to ponder rather than quilt.

I felt inundated with the weight of all that had been and the threat of what could be. There was a risk in having faith in his words, in trusting what I'd heard last night. Because if at any point he changed his mind, the dream would be crushed. The rug would be swept out from under whatever plans we made for our new future. But I chose to have faith. To trust that this was what is meant to be. Because I felt God behind me this time. I had reached out for His hand, and with Him beside me, all things are possible. This very event that took place last night, ugly as it looked and sounded to be, was the unlatching of a door.

I'd held this dream of freedom I'd held since I was eight years old when I first expressed to my mother the truth of what my father was and was not. A dream that had only grown since my mother and I tasted the freedom in our footsteps up north.

When the new year had begun, I'd intensified my call up to God. Remembering His loving, guiding stirring in my spirit that's told me, "Yes, *but not yet,*" back in the fall, I set out believing with all my heart that what I needed He would create for me. From that day on, I'd entrusted my Angels and God with my dream of freedom and followed the depths of my heart. I followed their stirrings in the depths of me to savor a new love for home in new ways and find honest compassion for my Dad. In these things, my faith and heart grew. I practiced manifestation, picturing what freedom looked like in my mind. I concentrated on the feeling of that truth, as if it was already here just in another time not so far away. I knew that one day it would happen. I knew it with my heart because God had placed that dream there. God plants dreams in our hearts to water them with us so that they'll grow beyond what we ever envision. His plans are always expansive and sure.

Life: Taking Inner Action

As I stepped down into the kitchen, I surveyed his demeanor to see where he stood. He held his ground. It was the same. I was pleasantly, tepidly, hopeful.

I turned to my friend, Barbara, and called her on the phone. I knew that she would grant me the guidance and focus I needed at this possibly pivotal moment in my life. Barb told me, "Visualize what you want, exactly how you want it. But it doesn't just take visualization. It takes more than that. It takes action. You have to take actions to make it happen for yourself." "I love you."

I needed to hear her words. They renewed my power to say to myself that I knew this moment, here and now, was the window of opportunity I had waited for all my life. I was gifted the chance, and I was going to take it by the reins with both hands.

It was real. And it was mine for the taking. I sat down with my notebook and made a plan. The only person who could reach him was me. Anyone else would judge his thoughts, and Mom was not who he turned to in this first step of choice, maybe because the choice impacted her. I felt a sense of comfort in his trust, that he finally opened a piece of himself to me that was more genuinely him than before. I believe the grace and compassion that God had been fostering in my heart for my dad was what led him to confide in me that night. He knew he could turn to me. I'd shown that no matter what he said or did, I was still loving him, still calm in the storm. *Somewhere deep inside, he must feel my love, right?* I may never know, but it meant something to me to be a safe place for him because everyone deserves that, no matter their nature.

Because he was seeking me for counsel to either affirm or deny an unconfident idea he held inside. I had one chance to do this right. I drew a hot bath, allowing the steam to take me away, and prayed long and hard. I could feel God's Loving hand reaching out to me.

I realized I had to have faith not just in God but in myself. I had to reach deep within myself and take action with courage, use my inner compass consciously as I coursed these uncharted skies. With careful courage and surrendering trust, it empowered me to take action. When I stepped out, dressed, and put pencil to paper, everything just came out right. I organized my thoughts, everything that needed to be said.

As an objective observer of their relationship all these years, I sat down with him and simply said something I'd come to understand, something fair and honorable to them both and most of all true. I told him that from my years of teaching, I discovered that some families are better versions of themselves, happier, when they are apart. But it was his choice to determine if that applied to the two of them. I told him that he and Mom spoke different languages in love, both giving and receiving in ways that neither saw or understood. Their hearts' expressions were like ships passing in the night. And it took work to find a way to speak and understand these differences. He'd have to choose if he wanted that.

He was quiet, listening as I spoke. When I was finished, he was immediately resolute. He was going to do it. He thanked me for sharing what I thought and walked out of the room with satisfaction in his steps. It was almost too smooth. That was a fearsome signal in my mind. Things weren't this easy with him. Was his need for me not real? Was his mind made up all along?

Suddenly, as he leaned back across the threshold of the room, his story shifted. "I'm glad you suggested this that I leave your mother. I'm going to do it. I'm not sure how she'll feel about your initiating it. Hopefully that's not harmful to your bond. Maybe she'll understand your support for me when I tell her I'm leaving." He shrugged nonchalantly. He was making his departure my choice, my idea.

I had to let it go if we were to be free. I knew what he was trying to do was throw a torch of damage toward my mom's and my relationship on his way out. He thrived on having power over us. He was aiming a weapon at our relationship to crack and poison it as he exited. I would never understand how he got pleasure from these things, so harmful and unseen.

What I did understand was the security that lied in Mom's and my relationship. I could handle whatever he threw. I knew our love was much stronger than that. The power of love is far stronger than the power of a man.

Reflection: Rainbows

There are rainbows everywhere up north. In the land, in the sky, twilight, and dawn's break. A rainbow appears across a million of the tiniest dewdrops of a spiderweb, together making one.

Most often, I see them reaching from the sky onto the land. In the early morning light, softly touching the deep blue violet clouds with shades of pink that blend down to the trees in cadencing splays of orange. It's like the sun stepped down from the sky and onto their bare winter branches for one awakening moment and then back up into the sky of the day.

Rainbows, to me, mean that God's hand is in this. The way they cascade down so often between Heaven and Earth in our sunrise and sunset tells me that His hand is in each rise and fall we meet. His hand is with ours on Earth as it is in Heaven. We just see it best when we pause to start and end the day. When we're closest to ourselves. Our spirit. To Him.

Reflection: Trust in Deep Water

To venture into uncharted waters is an uncomfortable feeling for me. I suppose it is for everyone. But it is for me, most of all with water. I cannot swim. And because it's not my strong-suit, I do not paddle board into the deep. To do so seems like a treacherous test of fate. A chance of testing my life jacket in a way that invokes fear from a place so primal I can't relate it to another person.

But today, I went. On the cool, smooth water, I pressed my limits. I don't want to live within the walls of my fears, and the only way to tear them down is to push them. So I did. As I paddled, I reached places I could see the dwelling depths, rich with its spiraling weeds that could catch my ankle and drag me in. I passed over areas where plant matter was so rich, I could see only black with streaks and swirls of emerald green so dark it would swallow you up, never to be found for some time to come. But I didn't allow myself too many of those thoughts about those deep-reaching places. As I paddled on, I realized trust is a choice. It's knowing the hazards, the risks, and triggers, yet choosing to be brave because it's worth it. You *live* for it. And by that, the rewards far outreach those limiting fears. You push past your own horizons beyond the places you ever imagined and dreamed possible for you. All begins with the deliberate choice of trust. In yourself, in your own life-jacket of sorts, in another, and ultimately in God. All lies in the discerning, deliberate, and empowering choice to trust.

Life: Planning

Who am I going to be in Michigan? I am going to be every part of the person I am. I'm going to be an expert on nature and attuned to that natural world that envelops my home and my soul. Whenever I seek it, all I have to do is step outside my door. What a gift.

I'll adore my land and its people in a way that touches my heart, fuels my soul, recharges my spirit. I'll see connection and inspiration in every new day. In the quiet start of the morning, the cool breeze through the afternoon as the weather changes with the passing hours, the culture of my people, my home, my family, the sunsets closing the days with a majestic finale and the nights with more stars in the sky than the eyes can count.

My spirit knew this northern place was home long before I knew it could ever be my forever home. I would look out at the lake, breathe in the woods, with a sense of home in my soul. A sense of knowing that this was the right place for me to be in every fiber of my being, every aspect of my heart and mind. My friends and even my logical mind told me that this remote place was a land with no opportunities for someone so young. But how can someone define opportunity? Was opportunity constrained to be so conventional? To me, opportunity meant to live authentically. It presented itself in this very moment more than it ever had before.

This very opportunity had been built through so many spontaneous choices, like volunteering at the local community dinner or running inside from the drizzling rain to share a dish and find a long-time friend at Thursday potluck. Opportunity was catching a glimpse of the eagle as he fished over the lake while the swans drifted gracefully in their timeless romance over a morning misty sunrise. Each one brings me from my mind, to the moment, and before my every sense. A love like this makes me come alive inside. It's the love of a place, a love for the truth I get to rest in that place, the me I get to be, that others see, that people love, I suppose in this place I learned what it means to find yourself.

There's been nowhere else I've felt more in touch with myself, my soul, my spirit, my sense of knowing, my inspiration and creativity. God gave me a powerful gift in these woods.

Life: Church Going

"If I'm going to leave, I'm going to need someone to take care of me. Your mother has done that the past thirty years. I know I can't function on my own."

"Okay. How do you plan to accomplish that?" I asked, awed and unsettled at his awareness and perplexed at where this was going.

"I'm going to do one of two things. I'm going to check into the senior independent living facility or I'll join a church. Because church people take you in. They feed you and give you things to do. They'd take care of me."

I couldn't help but wonder at the sincerity of his growing faith, and what was possible. What I did know was that his heart was coming into God's hands. I had faith that God would work wonders with Dad's time with Him.

Reflection: Vice

A vice can be something that numbs the pain, an object to reach for that gets you through. At times, it's an entity to keep you from losing. Some instances, it's a way to numb feelings too tender or deep, too wrought or ugly to face. Some don't know how, so they turn to the vice.

The vice creates a frenetic path that takes one anywhere but to the place of healing . . . until they awaken. Perhaps, for some, that was the purpose of the vice from the start. A blanket of security to cover the places that are to be faced and found. Perhaps there's a vice we all turn to within. One that points to a greater state of healing, of feeling, that we desire at the soul. Have courage.

If someone were to ask me, I'd probably say I don't have a vice. I don't deny my feelings or hide from parts of myself. I don't. And yet parts of my life have hidden themselves from me. And so in comes the vice. For sometimes, vices come along to help us make a million attempts to fill the void until we awaken and we see that the only thing we can fill those spaces with is light. Do you hear me? The light is love.

You see, in some deep-rooted part of me, I found a sense of duty. Rooted in love, I felt the need to heal my abuser. I felt I must make him feel my love. I must make him feel love itself. I ached with that need. The thought that if only I could achieve that for him, I could release him. All of this abuse, shame, torture, secrets, lies, would be worth it. I didn't want it because I needed his love for me. I needed it because I loved him. I wanted it because I understood his abuse was a signal that he could not be whole. If only I could make him feel again. Something besides the bleeding poison of resentment. Awaken his soul to his heart. So he could understand love too.

That iteration of empathetic compassion drove me towards every vice I've ever known. Fragments of love. Iterations of him clothed in different skin. Without awareness of it, I was driving myself into the same wall again and again. Each time left me no longer standing inside. And yet I needed to try. I needed to know that I did *everything* to save a person from themselves, from their dark unknowns. Show them their long-lost lights and cradle them with care.

But there comes a time when every spiritual warrior becomes wise. A series of moments that culminate into power yet unknown. I wasn't healing any of them. Even my father, and no amount of passion and investment, light and love, could change that.

The final thing about a vice is that in order to break its hold it has over you . . . the very first step to survival, thriving, release, freedom, *living* . . . is recognizing it. I see my vice now. I stare it in the faces. I feel it from my heart. And for every time I reach toward it, I vow to let it go. It holds me in a past and in a cycle that always had the same outcome.

Life: Change

My father may not have been close to me or affectionate, I may not have felt at home with him, but the way he'd come to share his thoughts and feelings with me gave me a sense of comfort. I felt trusted, and that's a big part of love.

I think when I'd shifted to compassion for my dad, things shifted between us. He opened up his mind and other parts than the dark side of his spirit. The black that hued right into grey and stayed there. He shared things he'd done and not done that he'd never told anyone on this Earth before. It helped me know him. It helped me understand that who he was now was who he had always been.

As he opened up, I felt the little girl coming alive inside me, grasping at that shoestring of hope for a connection. Because I did love him. I wanted this time to be different. Foolish as it seemed to want that, I believed that even just a semblance of love shared was possible. God could do anything.

What I was doing with that hope, though, was not honoring myself and the truth I knew. No matter how much I gave of myself, my dad was not going to bond with me in the way that I longed for. Whether God was in his life or not, he still had the psychology to work toward controlling and manipulating those close to him. My hope made my heart vulnerable to being intentionally hurt for sport. Made it vulnerable to a one-sided relationship. In all that hope and trying, I'd lose myself every time. Only to rebuild myself and try again. It wasn't until I stopped that I would realize all this waste of energy, that my heart could only create powerful good in the world if I didn't subjugate it. Our hearts are whole and creative in this world when we respect ourselves and shine our light, no matter how that may threaten others' shadows.

Reflection: Pine Growth

Leaving abuse is like walking through fire. It takes courage to burst through the flames, but you know deep within that's the only way to go. Those flames burn you in many places as the culmination of an old life gone sears your skin. Family, friends, places, things, memories, plans, loss. But once you're through, the smoke clears. And you realize the fire burned what needed to burn. It was making way for the best yet to come. Your life's dreams.

There's a special tree that lies within our woods. It requires this very process to exist. It's called the jack pine. Its seed can lay dormant for twenty years, poised for the moment when the way has been cleared for it to awaken from its slumber. When fire strikes, the old familiar forest is gone as if it never were, leaving char in its wake. The fire awakens the seed. And yet, in the sunshine springs the start of the tall, sturdy new growth of a tree who was made for this moment, who needed it to live. Who's basking in the light of its first pure rays of sun. The new growth of life that envelops around it will look never the same. And that may be the fiercest flame of all.

As my mother and I led our lives from the heart, most everything we owned was acquired through our hearts as well. That made the process of moving more painful. But, like the jack pine, we knew that to make room for the light of a new day, we must make room by casting away most of our past. Slow burns are damaging, but they don't accomplish what's needed for a forest due for a clean break. We knew to clear our home hot and hard. We made decisions like rapid fire. Take. Go. Keep. Toss. Pack. Donate. I watched as I carried my own meaningful mementos of my childhood to be rolled away. Parcels of my hopes were cast off to lighten the load, no longer as important as the immediate need at hand. We both did it. We had to. For if we did not, we'd be taking toxic remnants of our past. Things that would clutter our new life with our old existence.

There was much but little we were able to take. Regrets plagued us for what was forsaken in the rush to rise up out of the ashes away from old home. Sadness and hurt over what was lost in the fire of burning away what once was. But the journey onward, upward surpassed those mementos and things because, after all, that's just what they were. And without them, we could be free and grow. They taught me just how little *things* matter in comparison to the memories they're tied to. Those weren't inseparable.

Life: **Bible Shock**

My father had fully moved into his new place. Yet here he was suddenly. I could feel the pit in Mom's stomach as her old car lurched up the drive and grinded to a halt just before the patio grill. Dad slowly made his way out, gathering a disheveled pile of bills from the front seat and the back, most of them late from sitting in his apartment unattended. His presence brought a wave of bristled hostility and coldness to the already suffocating air of what used to be our home, and I braced myself for what words he had to bring with him.

"Here, I got this for you." He handed me a black box. It seemed to be a gift, though unwrapped. I could tell it was a Bible right off from reading the lid. I was shocked.

Confused, "Thank you" quietly was all I could say. I took it to the end of our living room, beside our mattress on the floor where we'd been sleeping since emptying the upstairs and held it a moment. My mind raced as he sat down with Mom with a dejected air and began pushing the well-known buttons of her feelings. Their interactions pained me, but for once I did not intervene or try to mediate or ease the tension. I engrossed myself in this moment of shock. I paused in a very surreal mix of disbelief and wonder as I lifted it out of the box.

Weeks ago, I'd had a vision. I always ran in the dark of night that was the wee hours of the morning. When the streetlights reflect on the shining bricks and the pavement is as black as the shadows that surrounded me. I'm sure, looking back, it wasn't my wisest era of exercise, but it sure was inspiring. To feel so hidden, reclusive in a world not yet awake or even able to see me in the streets as I ran. Every beat of my footsteps charging out emotion, passion, hope, despair. Half the time I ran, I spent in prayer. Most people didn't know that about me. It was what I love about my runs. What made the dark work for me so well. It was like having your eyes closed, but your body moving just enough that it could shut off your mind.

That particular morning, I'd set off down my old brick street. The bricks shined ever brighter as the thick smell of rain filled my senses from just hours ago. And a vision flashed across my eyes. A bible in a vibrant shade of pink. Simple yet ornate. Natural yet elegant. It was me. When it came across my mind's eye, I'd recognized it, like I'd dreamt of it before.

And here it was, tucked inside this box my father gave to me, exactly as I'd envisioned. With the detail of the fine, deep pink leaf engraved binding and the soft leather pink cover that begged to be read and cherished, I felt like my dad knew me and thought of me for the first time. It touched a piece deep inside me, the little girl who always simply wanted her daddy's love. My insides churned with the old familiar chains of questions that only tightened as they came. Was this an act of love? How did he know this was the Bible I'd envisioned? Could he be forming a connection with God? Was he manipulating me with this? Inside the front cover, I read the words, "Love, Daddy." Two words that had not naturally stood alone from him, least of all together. Two words I wanted to see for 26 years of my life written across the cover page of the most personal book I could think of.

In the back, there was a piece of paper, a small sheet of paper. It held an inspirational message and a quote from the Bible, a catered quote from different places of scripture he'd learned from the groups I'd suggested for him. "The perfect Father . . . has given each one of us supernatural grace . . . some with the grace to be teachers . . . And their calling is to nurture and prepare all . . . to contribute to the growth of all. Ephesians 4: 6, 7, 11, 12, 16"

Discord churned through my senses right next to a sense of awe. I was stricken. I turned to my father, taking him in, trying to make sense of this. He was pushing the right buttons in an artful motion of the mind that sent her emotions to the ledge of anger and hurt and worthlessness. He knew how to use words and body, to impose control and stir confrontation. This act of kindness was reflective of the man I always believed was inside him, the man that I felt. And yet, across the room in this moment among all the others, he was still him. I stayed back. Silent. *What did this mean? What do I accept? What is safe?*

When they were through, I walked him out to our driveway. He said nothing of the Bible, instead telling me spited office stories, questioning me, trying to manipulate me. Confused and searching, I thanked him for the Bible. He stood taller and boasted. He was still him. *But what was it inside him that gave this to me? And was it real?*

He left, but the Bible plagued me. It confronted my mind, heart, and spirit for all the questions it raised about him. When I returned inside, I sat down, holding it, facing it. And I sobbed. I sobbed for all the mirages of love that gesture embodied. I sobbed for the hope that resided in each one. I sobbed for the hope for him that I had to let go of again and again only to still hold on. I cried for what I wanted all those years and for my unconditional love that was unkindly unaccepted and ill-received. My heart that was played with and put down and the way it grew weaker yet stronger through those experiences. Like a bone growing stronger from its little fractures.

"Why did he do that?" I asked my mother, hearing a little girl in my whimpered question. I felt conflicted in a multitude of directions. She held me. I felt like to accept this gift was to at once resolve a lifetime of heartache and betray my own truth I had taken years to accept.

Life: **Papa's Arms**

In times of stress, I believe the ones who are bound most tightly to our hearts have a way of knowing, a way of being there across the veil. In the midst of our laborious and tumultuous move, Mom and I faithfully visited my grandma, as we always had. She was a spirited woman, perceptive of even the slightest dismay or quiet look. Her heart was tender in a sensitive kind of way. Sassy and cheerful, she brought as much joy to my day as I brought to hers. And when I'd fall ill or stray away from seeing her for a week or two, a sweet card adorned with stickers would come in the mail to cheer me and remind me I'm loved, loved especially by her. My grandma was special. We all need someone like that in our lives who makes us feel adored, whom we adore right in return. Always.

On this particular day, the busyness of grandma's voice as she talked over bills with mom, and the lull of the ceiling fan as it churned faithfully overhead sent me into a dozey sleep that my body yearned for. I was exhausted. Physically for sure the daily strains of the move, but mentally and emotionally, too, from the hundreds of decisions that the move and its purging required. It was draining my well.

The women in the other room, discussing the mail, I drifted off, but soon I woke softly from my slumber. I opened my eyes just a little. I was comforted by the feeling of an arm around me. An arm of a man who felt safe and sound, gentle and secure. I could see that arm. Long, dark hairs wispily covered suntanned skin that led down to strong, worn hands with fingernails that had ripples which went from tip to tail. I recognized this form with a strike of awe. My papa! I felt the essence of my grandfather's love, and at once my heart felt whole again. He was here with me, showing me he's always by my side. That I'm safe in his loving arms.

Life: **Bible Reconciles**

In the weeks and months thereafter, that Bible haunted me. The only thing I could do was pray. What am I meant to learn from this God? Please show me the way.

A compilation of memories flooded through my mind as that Bible worked on my conscience. I realized that my father was a broken man. I'd faced the repeated reality long ago that he wasn't capable of love. But his blind hatred had blinded me. It kept me from seeing in my youth that he didn't harbor hate out of truly hating me. As I grew older, I came to realize that this was all he's been capable of being.

When he opened his eyes to me, he let a little light in somewhere. That's where those confusing statements came from, out of the blue. The ones I always remembered but never allowed myself to take to heart. Like the time he snapped a picture of me out of the blue. He said, "I want that picture to remind me of the best decision I ever made. It wasn't going into medicine or choosing to practice in a small town. It wasn't my first wife. When your mom asked me to have you, I was a little drawn back because Marcy had leukemia, and I had my job, and I thought with the family and work it would be too much. But you have turned out to be the best decision I have ever made."

In his own way, that was how he told me he loved me. And that picture stood in a frame in his apartment. When I saw it, my insides screamed because for so long I'd only known that he couldn't love me, that he wouldn't, and that expressions like these were fleeting. Now, somehow, I'd become one of the people he respected the most.

As I healed my way into the new, I began my own more personal inward journey. Over the weeks, it began to dawn. I can't say it was a moment when I knew. More so, a realization that settled into my heart until I had to act upon it. I realized that God was facing me with a choice. To choose love. Not in the giving sense I'd always seen it. That was the easy way for me, but in the sense of accepting.

Accepting love was something I had come to block for a long, long time. It wasn't healthy, but it happened. Without even realizing it, I had numbed myself to words of admiration, care, and respect from most everyone in my world. I didn't do it on purpose. It just became a habit of protection. By not feeling loved in the first place, I saved myself from the feeling of death that was learning the love was not sincere, that the love which seemed to exist wasn't real. And somewhere along the way, down that fearfully safe road, I came to believe that I wasn't worthy of love. Because to have unreal love many times over from many places makes a person feel that love for them must not be possible, must not be for you.

It was time to change that. It was time to accept love again. Any way I could find how. It would require a growing in trust, clarity, self-worth, and revival. Right here, my father was presenting to me his love. Not in the form that I had wanted, but in the ways he knew how. In the way my father *could* love me. It was now my choice to accept his love.

Reflection: Heart of Colors

My mother and I used to listen to the Dolly Parton song, "Coat of Many Colors" on our many road trips up north, singing along to the familiar words. Smiling all the while.

The song talks about how Dolly's mother sewed together a coat for Dolly from a box of rags that someone had given to their family. It was the way for Dolly to have a new coat, and it was sewn with love. I knew that if we lived that life in those days, my mom would do the same for me; it was that kind of love.

I think that's the kind of love God has for us. He notices where our heart is feeling cold, and he patches together what we need from the gifts we are given in this life. Gifts come in many forms. In my life, I see them most of all in people and in nature.

God heals my heart through romantic reveries of every fiber of nature I can imagine. He never ceases to surprise even my imagination with what is in store. Moments and meanings my heart and soul need in a language almost too deeply full for our language of words.

His work in people is another kind of magic. It's where he weaves needle and thread much like the making of that "Coat of Many Colors" to form something that warms us, protects us where we need it most. I see it in most every person's path I cross. I see it in my own.

It seems to me most every person has some void in their life or another. Not one life is perfect for it wouldn't be beautifully Earthly if it were. A woman grows up without the love of her sister, and yet no matter where she goes, the dearest girlfriends find her. A boy hasn't any acceptance from his parents, but from a friend, a teacher, a coach, he finds acceptance of himself. A girl grows up with a father who is unable to love her in a healthy way, breaking her down in ways in the meantime. Yet, incredible men cross her path and see her worth and show her what a true-hearted man is; how that feels, in little pieces sewn with love.

God does these things.

Life: **Paul**

In the early days of visiting the north woods, just as we do today, my mother and I enjoyed getting up bright and early. Up north, when you rise in the early hours you have the great privilege of watching the world wake up. The light ebbs and glows into the sky with its soft timbers in the east bringing warmth to the crisp cool air outside our window. Fresh air that smells of cedar and pine when the wind blows from the woods and of earth and water when it blows from the lake. Both scents equally cleansing to the mind, body, and soul. As the crisp air takes on its daylight warmth, the birds respond by starting their routines. Pairs of ducks and loons and swans appear on the lake through the foggy mist. The ever-present mosquitoes silently plink against the windowpane to make their presence, and their undiscriminating hunger, known. The occasional ground squirrel scurries near the trees, full of nervous energy. Then, the human inhabitants of this beautiful place begin to venture out into the day.

One came just before seven o'clock in the form of a small tan truck, a former executive who chose to slow down the pace of life. A longtime friend now, at times, that little tan S-10 would swerve toward me playfully as I went for my morning run, its driver hollering, "Hey you know the speed limit around here's only about twenty!" or, "Run a few miles for me!" That little S-10 was up in its years, one might wonder why a man who put it to use wouldn't trade in for a larger, newer, shinier model. But then if you could peer inside the cab of that truck and see tucked inside the dash, right alongside the speedometer, you'd find a photo of the man who made him, the idol he adored. That truck carried on a piece of him wherever this son went. And that entrusted truck also parked each night at the home of his widowed mother before returning home from work at the local hardware store. The eyes of this son behind its wheel shined with such a love you could feel the catch in your own chest as he spoke to you about his mother and father. Such devotion and reverence for one's parents is something not often seen and touching beyond words. That truck was something I respected him deeply for. For all that meaning behind the clock-work of his ways, I appreciated each time I saw it.

Life: **Marshall and Annie**

After the seven o'clock passing of Paul's truck would come the next inhabitant of these piney woods. This individual also came like clockwork, but he and his companion passed by foot. He embodied a distinguished gentleman. His honorable steps held an air of self-respect and refinement. From a button-up shirt, to an auburn leather belt depicting deer in the woods, he fit into the landscape that surrounded him. Yet, I could see he'd been outside of the vast yet small world that was the woods because his canvas-colored pants were bound by a shining army buckle. A forest green woolen cowboy hat shaded his face with a swatch of white horse hair tucked in the side. His ever-calm expression was framed in grey-white hair that held a gentle wave above a neatly trimmed beard.

There are some people who, when you first see them, you know. Something inside tells you that they're special. Or rather they're going to be special to you. I found myself captivated by this man and drawn to him in a way that made me wonder what it would be like to know him; a pull to know his story.

How do you act on a feeling like that? There's only one way. I had to introduce myself. His distinguished presence reflected in his speech, but the more often I approached him, step for step, his reserved kindness unfolded into jovial camaraderie, sharing sharp wit and vast wisdom.

Marshall shared with me the story of how he got his dog. Stories tend to show the reasons for things. Maya's story told the reason for the wild spirit in her eyes. It told the reason they had been paired together is because Marshall and Maya shared a common resonance of spirit and of drive.

Several years before, when Marshall and his wife, Annie, wanted a dog, they chose to adopt a shelter dog. Marshall had an interest in civics and a heart for stories that mattered, so naturally, he followed the news. When Marshall read about Hurricane Katrina rescue dogs, the story spoke to his heart. He wanted to bring one of those dogs into his family. In these north woods, though few people ventured, let alone southern rescues.

So, Marshall frequented the shelter, watching for a dog with the right disposition, until one day, he found a dog who looked right through you in the spirit of a wolf. She had a story too. As a white Inuit, Maya's kind was bred back to the wolf every fourth generation to maintain her instinctive connection to her heritage. What's more is that, after beginning her life as a house pet, Maya had spent two years surviving in the woods before she was found and brought to the animal shelter. As I intently listened to Marshall recount her story, it seemed to me that Maya's years in the wild matched the trials of that Category 5.

It was easy to see that Maya was a driven survivor, but also she was free. Maya's eyes bore a voracious tenacity that asserted she could highly surpass any trial or challenger. I was both in awe and intimidated by her, sure to keep my hands out of reach, in case for a moment, she decided she didn't like me. It wasn't that I didn't trust her, but I had a healthy respect for the wild heart that beat deeply within her. Trust from Maya was earned, so when the day finally came that her eyes softened and her head bowed in recognition of a friend, I felt honored. Though she was robed in fur, I was in the presence of a great. Marvelously, magnetically, it seems, greats tend to find one another. That's the reason Marshall and Annie found Maya.

Marshall treated life as a school for thought, thus deepening himself into an even more richly dimensional person. He held ideals like, "How lonely the rich must be for not knowing who their real friends are." Serving at community meals, on boards and committees, teaching and contributing seemingly everywhere, his value of service was a way of life. He appreciated the heartfelt corners of the world that held meaning, and remembered each one with a lively, animated story. He took initiative to rectify the world, like the time he noticed the rusted road sign around the bend. Marshall called the county office, propped up a ladder, and painted it back to life himself. Marshall spoke up for causes that matter. He taught people, truly taught them, by endowing them with the skills to do things themselves because he believed true leadership was to empower. He said what he meant and meant what he said. He was unafraid to draw lines in the sand to stand by his friends, even when what's right wasn't easy. He put on parties because he felt life and people ought to be enjoyed. He told stories in every detail because the details are where the story lies. He was there for those who could not do for themselves. He invented works of art, a forever engineer of intelligent plans and fine works.

Hearing the way Marshall lived his life, thought, acted, who he was intertwined with his life philosophies, and something beyond all these things, made me feel more myself. In him, I'd found, incredibly, someone who felt and thought like me; someone I aspired to be like. Marshall's wife shared his depth, and like the unfolding of a flower with time, Annie's heart opened to us as well.

Maybe because she was quiet, observant, Annie could pick up on the things going on in a room that most people wouldn't notice. She sensed other people's feelings keenly. She saw the truths that lied beneath the surface and persisted to bring them to surface. She persisted in what mattered most to her with a sweet and tender heart. Her strong moral pillar matched her husband's. With a willful and fiery spirit, she knew who she was and what she believed in, and for these things, she had strong boundaries. All these qualities I found in Annie, I came to deeply respect.

My mind traces back to one of what turned out to be many holidays together, this one Easter. Annie walked in the door, her creamy faux fur coat wrapped around her shoulders and her wispy white hair. Marshall followed closely behind in his HSC ball cap wearing a twinkling smile. As he tucked away her walker and purse, I gently greeted Annie with a caring hand and asked if I could take her coat. The satin lining slipped right off, and as it did, she pulled me in close for a hug. She said, "It's going to work out. Know that." Annie had been thinking of Mom and me and the life changes we'd shared with her. Worrying about us so, her care warmed my heart. Over the course of our visits, we'd become like grandparents and granddaughter to one another.

"Thank you. I know it will be." I smiled.

Annie gazed thoughtfully out the snowy window, her hand to her chin. "I'm gonna keep going." she quietly said to herself. "I can. I will." Annie turned to me and reached out her left hand that always wore a pearl ring. She pulled me in close so that we were nose-to-nose and looked at me intently with her own periwinkle crystal blue eyes. "It's going to work out. I pray for you."

"Thank you Annie. That means so much. And I pray for you too. Always."

"Young people, they give us inspiration. We need that inspiration to keep going. And you inspire me." Grandma wants you to know something very important. I love you." Her hand still holding mine, she patted it on my leg with tears in her eyes. "Always remember that. Even when I'm not with you. Okay?"

"Okay. I will. And I love you with all my heart. Your love means the world to me. You're right, it will work out. I look forward to being here with you. You're so special to me." I pulled her closer and kissed her on the cheek. She nodded, a frog in her throat as family and friends gathered to the table in conversation.

It touched me to know that Annie had been thinking so deeply of us, troubled by our troubles. She'd taken our situation to heart and to God out of love for us. And her love really did mean the world, as did the rest of the group that gathered around the table that evening. She made me feel loved with that same open depth time and time again. That, to me, was inspirational.

Stories are a way of sharing ourselves and how we came to be, what we believe and what we do not. There's a sense of camaraderie in sharing stories over sleepy cups of coffee, lively dinner tables, and breezy porches overlooking the street and the lake.

On evenings when we shared stories over the dinner table, Marshall always blessed the food with these words he seemed to live by. "Lord please bless this food that we are about to receive and the hands that prepared it. And remember our servicemen, especially those that gave the ultimate sacrifice. Help us to remember that we serve you by serving others through generosity and kindness. To help us remember to always treat our friends with care and respect."

Hearing Marshall and Annie's stories nourished me. But it was more than their tales I loved, it was them. Mom and I soaked Marshall and Annie up in the same way, taking in the soulfulness of their eyes, their expressions, their voices.

Marshall was the leader of storytelling. In his jovial smile and shining, sparkling eyes you could see right through to his kind soul. Marshall could tell a story like no other, and he had caches of them to tell. He was a bottomless well of wisdom, and the passion in his yarning of a tale, the lively expressions of his face, created pure magic.

Finer details tell great things about people. The geography of a face is one of them. The unique wrinkles in Marshall's skin fascinated me. I studied them as I listened. The way they folded to tell the story made it come to life. Marshall did not have deep creases between his eyes. Instead, he had smile wrinkles. He had lines all across his forehead drawing straight up from his salt and pepper brows all across to his wavy white hair that moved with every detail as he spun his tale. He made me feel like I was right there with him.

Marshall's earthy eyes were a golden brown that melted into mossy green until you met the ring around their edges that were like the deep blue of the ocean, framing it all together. It was as if he held the wisdom of the world in those eyes. But wisdom in its greatest sense because it was garnered through a lens of humanity, humility, and utmost care. What else was special about those eyes was you had to look deeply into them to see their many colors. Light illuminated every part of them as they gazed straight back at you, from the depths of one soul right into the depths of your own. Marshall was cordial as a friend, loving as a confidant, tender as a father. That's the love that illuminated from this reserved and giving man.

"Well, you tell them Marshall." Annie often said. We knew she didn't tell many tales in large part because she'd had a mini stroke a few years earlier, but oftentimes I wondered if most of all she just liked listening to him. For the way she sat poised in her chair, her face quietly enthralled in their memories, in his voice, in his telling of it. Just as we were. Her fluffy soft white hair swooped a gentle wave across her forehead and ears framing the pretty face that Marshall had fallen for sixty years ago, before their snowy wedding day at his alma mater. Her clear ocean-blue eyes would sparkle like a suncatcher as she gave you her signature wink and smile. One that brandished her entire face and somehow spread across right onto yours.

After all these years, it was charming to see how much joy she took in the yarning of his tales. Annie's eyes would twinkle with a nod to us that said, *This is about to get good.* Each one of us were empathetic, so when Mom and I empathized through a painful story, Annie would notice our feelings. She'd lean across the table to take our hands with a tight, assuring squeeze. Her heart held ours through that hand.

Some stories, when you hear them, make you believe a little more in fate. Marshall and Annie's meeting was one of those stories. It was an evening out of the ordinary. Home for the weekend from Michigan State, Marshall found himself without his steady girl to take to the group date among friends. As synchronicity would have it, his girlfriend's mother phoned the girl down the road. Annie could use a date.

After that night together, their futures had shifted. Like a fresh new lens slipped over the view of life. Marshall wasn't dating his girlfriend anymore. Annie was the only woman he could see. I can't help but wonder if what the young man saw in her back then was that big and tender heart that felt so powerfully for others; that he recognized and valued her immense capacity to love. I believe it was the depth behind Marshall's eyes that enabled him to recognize the depth in Annie's reflecting back to him. Two equally yoked souls.

Caught in a snowstorm on an evening right before Christmas, Marshall and Annie were married at Michigan State. Ploughing and trudging through quickly piling snowbanks, their attendants and closest friends made their way into the chapel. What they found was stilling, stirring. To this day, friends remarked at the way the church glowed romantically by candlelight. Annie in her white dress and mitten muff, her bridesmaids in red and green dresses, the boughs and poinsettias setting the stage for the holiday. But, I imagine, all that beauty vanished from sight when the bride entered the room, when Marshall and Annie's eyes fixed on each other. Just before Marshall had to report for duty the next month, their honeymoon was a visit to see Marshall's mother "one car at a time" Annie said with a fond yet *glad-we-made-it* grin.

There are some couples who hold a sense of magnetic attraction. That little something that shows they were meant to be, as if it were fated in the stars. Perhaps it's the way they look at each other, or the way they look out for each other, the investment they have in each other's dreams, appreciation for who one another was through and through. So many little things connect the dots in a constellation of pure love. Marshall and Annie had these things. The more I loved them myself, the more time I shared with them, the more I got to see what this love looks like. Feel the pulse of it. Reaffirm my faith in it.

I believe every person has a different capacity for how much love they're able to give and receive. Some less, and some more. Different measures don't make any one person better or worse. It makes them different in what they need and experience in love.

I believe having an equal capacity for love is the most important facet of a relationship. Because when two people of different capacities are put together, it seems one is often, in some way, left unfulfilled. Yet when two people fit together in the measures of their hearts, no song is left unsung. The essences of each other's hearts are synchronized. This kind of love was Marshall and Annie.

When Annie was young, the one thing her father feared most was that she would marry some boy who would take her away. When Marshall came along though, her father entrusted him. The kind of love for Annie that must have him to be able to let her go. The kind of respect for Marshall to allow his dreams to carry her away. And away they went. Marshall took the cattle farmer's daughter much farther from home than perhaps either of them anticipated.

Marshall was esteemed for his meritable wit and character, and his lustrous career in the military took them from Kentucky to Switzerland to Germany, where later their daughters were born, to France, to Korea, to South America, to so many corners of the globe that by the time he retired, they both had become rich within of the wonders of the world. The glow in their eyes when they spoke of the lush green countryside of Switzerland, the people of Germany, the places in America, their way of living together yet often apart, told me that those adventuresome times were their prime. I was captivated in their memories, enchanted, as if I were there with them. My heart touched by the echoes of their magic. Every true love, every good love, has a measure of magic.

Annie came from a line of passionate women, and she was proud of it. Her family farm had one very large, very mean bull. That bull would push Annie's mother around when she went out to the field, and she didn't like it. One day, Annie's dad went to town. That left her mother to manage the farm. It just so happens that this was a day that bull chose to push Annie's mother to the ground, and she wasn't having any of it! This was the last time! Mother marched right into the house, picked up the family shotgun stowed by the door, returned to the field, and shot that bull right between the eyes! That was enough of that. Annie's spirit danced each time she told that story. I could hear it a hundred times and never tire of it for watching her come alive at the memory. It was a part of her.

Marshall was raised just twenty miles away in a neighboring town. By several years, he was the youngest of three boys. A novel case in his era, Marshall was a child of divorce. The adjustments required of that division made for inconstancy in Marshall's childhood. It's not for us to know which qualities lie within the bounds of nature or nurture. Sometimes nature and nurture blur and weave indiscriminately, but all that came from that seemed to drive within him a deep foundation of independence, strong will, and drive.

I thought about the sadness Marshall must have felt then, and perhaps the responsibility shouldered for those who needed him. The wisdom and compassion that he garnered were the viewpoints from which he chose to lead. It wasn't common for a child to have a divided home in those days, much less one separated across the entire country. "When my parents got their divorce, I had no choice but to move to Florida with my mom."

"My mother worked two jobs to keep up with our bills when I was young, so to keep me out of trouble, I tagged along with my brothers much of the time, which I'm sure they weren't always too fond of. But if I was good, then she would give me a quarter to go see the show up at the theater on the weekend. Most every weekend I made sure I earned that show, and I would stay there all night. Even after the movie ended, I would just sit and watch the empty picture screen. Until they closed and I knew it was about time for my mother to come home. Even now, when I can't sleep, I go back there, to that blank screen, just because it was sooo boring! Something about sitting there with nothing to look at but that blank screen put me clear out in nothing flat." He said with a chuckle, but something after in his eyes as he sighed out that laughter said those were hard times too. The layers of a soul.

"When I was young, we moved a lot. And because we crossed into a different state, they were teaching different things. So, where I was once getting As and Bs in Maria, I was suddenly failing reading in Florida because in Michigan, they hadn't taught it yet. Well, the principal said they were just going to have to hold me back a year; there wasn't anything else they could do. But my teacher said she didn't think that was the right thing for me. She didn't want me to be held back from my group of peers my age. She stayed with me after school every day for a year to catch me up to my grade, and I got caught up. I may not have liked it that much at the time, but I sure appreciated it later."

Marshall remembered the impacts people had made in his life with appreciation. I marveled at how he remembered and valued every single one for all of his born days with an undying measure of appreciation. Seeing that in him impacted me. It showed a key element to life-long happiness is seeing and remembering when someone or something changed you, recognized you, helped you get to where you are today. Staying connected to those people is important, for the value of yourself and those special people who loved a new piece into your heart. When we stay aware of these gratitudes the way that Marshall has through his lifetime, we remain not only humble, but also aware of the many gifts God has given us along our way.

Marshall appreciated the finer points of our remote world, just like me. The quiet, small beauties of nature, the things that some people don't even notice. It was one of the ways I identified with him deeply. "It's most fun to snowmobile at night." He sat back in his chair, beginning, "On a clear night when all the stars are twinkling in the sky and you have the moon casting light down on the trails. There's plenty of brightness to see your way. It casts a huuunndred different shades of blue and grey onto the snow. It's beeaaauuuutiful." Annie smiled remembering it too. "And when you shut the machine off at night, it's aaaabsoooluuuutely silent. Very peaceful." His appreciation for the simple things, for nature made me glow inside. Knowing someone else shared my vision made me appreciate him all the more.

"Annie was afraid for falling off the snowmobile, so she had me make her a leather harness. It strapped around her waist and went up over my shoulders, so if we went up over a bump and anything went wrong, well, we were both going together," he chuckled. He nurtured her safety and security, made her feel thought of, and cared for her in the ways she needed him without ceasing. It was equal in measure to how she tended to his feelings and concerns, how she always wanted to be near him. It amazed me as I watched that kind of love unfold even after sixty-one years of marriage.

When Marshall and Annie lived abroad, Annie made sacrifices to be with Marshall. In the form of not-so-patiently awaiting his return. She would find a way onto his base to live in the dorm with him against the rules. She'd drive across the country of France with a baby in the back because it'd been too long since they'd parted. Their love was powerful. It was one that showed equally yoked souls do exist, and they thrive together.

I imagine the changing nature of the military tested Marshall and Annie's marriage at times. But it bonded them together all the more, sharing those times. They were experiencing cultures and each other in new ways as they embraced life together in the midst of navigating harsh realities. It was interesting to me how they each showed the same kind of love to each other in the different ways each other needed. Annie's faithfulness came through standing by him in those times of warzone unknowns when all her heart carried her feelings away with her. Marshall was faithful through gentle patience, especially as Annie aged.

From loving Marshall and Annie, I learned that love brings out the best in all of us. It opens up our hearts to shine from within. We all deserve it. Love, even simply genuine care, is the kind of gift that's received like ripples atop still water. Boundlessly.

Those ripples between Annie and us extended ever farther with the passage of time. Whenever we'd part, I'd kneel down to hug Annie, and she'd pull me in close. She'd squeeze my hand and look intently into my eyes with the meaning of every word she said. "Grandma has something to say. I love you, remember that. Okay honey? I pray for you every day, that things will work out alright." To know we were in her vast heart and in her prayers, meant the world. "I love you so much you could be a part of me." she'd say. The firm grasp of Annie's hand sent a calming, assuring surge of love through me, like a hug in the spirit. Her soft voice and her eyes held my gaze, to make those loving reminders last a lifetime, more than that.

Marshall loved us the same way. "I love you." came in seldom, spontaneous moments that made your heart catch. When he did, his words were gentle yet powerful, just like his embrace. It also rested in remarks like, "You take care of yourself so we can have more time together." What's more is I learned from Marshall that love is best spoken through the eyes. Love poured through his eyes when he looked at us. They spoke with more meaning than words could ever say.

Their love transcended.

Annie knew how I revered Marshall. But she also saw him. She told me how highly Marshall thought of me; how special I was to him and how much respect he had for me. I felt as if, in some cosmic way, I was like the granddaughter he didn't have, and I hoped in some small way, I could carry on the legacy of his vast heart. I wondered if Marshall felt that too. The shining in his eyes told me yes.

There really are few people on this earth with whom I truly resonate. So when I find that, it's a precious gift I treasure. Marshall and Annie's presence in my life enriched my heart because they placed in it an anchor of love that bore the weight of abiding friendship. Hearing the stories of their lives, spending time with them taught me the power of relationships because with them, my soul finally felt at home amongst people.

I believe God speaks in people, in colors, in the stars, in every element of nature and beyond, if only we look to see. He finds people whose hearts sing the same song and brings them together with purpose. God pieces families and friends together, filling voids and mending hearts, growing them. We found in each other the deep, true nature we needed at a time it mattered most. And when God binds people through love, every heart grows both within and together. That's what I found in Marshall and Annie's friendship. And so much more . . .

Life: Love Empowers

Stepping out of the new school and onto the street towards home, I took in the breeze and the trees that lined our small city's streets. The sugar gum tree still stood tall on the same ground it had when I was a girl playing at my elementary school. The one built in 1920 with long coat rooms that adjoined each classroom and beautiful woodworking lining plaster walls. Marble steps that bowed where thousands of children's feet had tread over the decades past. There were problems in that building that this tree reminded me of: four-inch-long roaches by the hundreds and asbestos too, but it was mine. A part of my childhood that I remembered as I looked up the street and spied a little blue truck driving down it. Another piece of my past I remembered fondly, with even more emotion. That truck didn't turn right towards home where I expected it to, and as it kept coming and my own right turn came, I wondered if I was wrong about what I'd seen, but I didn't dare look back.

I was wearing the red skinny jeans my coworker had given me in January. Her husband had purchased them for her for Christmas. She said that she knew I could wear them. When I did, I always thought of her. They were pretty, and so was she, from the inside out. I pulled my coat closer as the brisk wind blew through the collar.

The color blue idled up beside me, its window already rolled down. "Hi Allie." I couldn't believe it.

"Hey Levi." I was happy he'd stopped.

"I just was driving home, and I saw someone walking, and I thought, I think that's Allie. If you want, I'll give you a ride home. I know you might want to get your walk in. That's okay too."

"Of course. Thank you." I did want my walk, but I wanted this more. "How did you recognize me?"

He grinned bashfully. "Your walk." I smiled back.

"And," he continued, "I thought to myself, you're about the only woman I know who'd wear red pants. Be confident like that. It's a good thing. They look nice on you. It's a good color."

"Hmm." I looked at him and then out the window, taking in a new compliment. "Thanks."

"How've you been Levi? How's your family? And Ally?" Ally Monroe, the small cat he'd taken in off the corner of his alley and Monroe Street, had brought a constant, gentle, playful companionship to his life that was good for him.

"Good, good. We're all good." He told me about his family, and then he asked about me. I told him of our changes. His smile fell in shock. It seemed he didn't know what to say, but most of all his eyes told he didn't know what to do. When he dropped me off that day, it was as if in a daze. He told me he'd call me. I thought it seemed moot now. But as always, I couldn't say no to his company. Not to him.

He texted me two days later, asking if he could come over to talk to me. I wondered what it could be. When he arrived, he was comfortable and at ease, chatting with Mom. He settled down into our living room rocking chair as if he always had. Then, with Mom still in the room, he turned to me and told me he'd been doing some thinking. He'd thought about the time we'd spent together and what I meant to him, choices he'd made, and timing, and life. He said there were these things he needed to say to me because he had to.

I sat, captivated in trepid shock. I couldn't believe his heart was so fully on his sleeve. After all this time, in front of my mother nonetheless! Feeling awkwardly out of place, she stood from her seat. "I'm going to go in the other room and give you two some space." He didn't bat an eye. He just acknowledged her with a nod and continued with these words.

"I know that you were it for me. I was just too comfortable in my ways. I didn't want to change my routines for you. But you . . . I had everything I could have ever asked for and more than I will ever know in you. And you're going to be the biggest regret of my life. You already are. Because I love you. And it takes you leaving for me to admit all of this to myself let alone say it all to you. Things are always better with you. I'm better with you. I see things more clearly. Life more clearly. You're so gentle and full of love, and I didn't make the time. And I'm sorry for that now because if I had, I wonder what could have been. And if you hadn't left, I don't think I ever would have done it. I would have kept along as things were and not thought about it because that was easy. But you were what I need. I just had too much ego to admit to myself that I needed you. There's never gonna be anybody else because there is no one else like you. You have always been so patient with me and understanding and sensitive and kind. People aren't like that. You make me better. And when you're gone it hurts. That's why I know it was you."

As he talked, I came to his side. I sat on the floor and rubbed his knee while he spoke. But he didn't stop. He just kept speaking until he'd said everything he'd come to say, and when he was through, his whole body sat still, his face with a faraway look as if he'd betrayed himself.

In that moment, my mind raced between telling him the truth and telling him a lie I thought would give him peace. I knew the truth was the only place to go. I owed it to him after his brutal honesty. So, I told him of my earnest feelings from the start. How I'd been confused about where he stood, so I pulled back, maybe too much. That he'd been in my heart from the beginning, never far away.

We went for a walk as we talked out our hopes and our fears, our thoughts and choices as the pathways of our friendship had unfolded since we met. Being so open was like breathing fresh air into my heart, my mind. Though I knew there was no future between us, I couldn't help but revel in it. He felt it too.

"You brought me back to the living Allie. You showed me how to live." And I knew. He felt it too. That the path we'd walked together had been pure and profound and meant for each other.

"You showed me what shared love feels like. And you allowed me to trust love again. That it doesn't go away." I replied.

He hugged me, and he didn't let go, but instead held me there for a time that I could have kept forever . . .*You could have me*, I wanted to say. I knew either one of us could make a bold move: me stay or him follow. Yet I knew it wasn't right or real for either one of us. Our love was but this reality between us we'd been pretending was tangible. If I stayed, I would live inside his box and never grow outside of nurturing him, never accomplish my life in the world. If he followed, he would lose his carefully built sense of security. More and more, our love was fading into the truth that it was not. Neither of us were ready to face it just yet because, for now, it was too good to let go.

We spent the coming weeks leading up to my move sharing evenings together when time allowed. Long talks, walks to new places in my town I'd never been but he wanted to show me. It was as if we were living a lifetime in a few short weeks. We both knew it would end, but we weren't thinking of that. Because now that the masks of trepidation were off, we were engulfed in the moment, in each other, in the memories we were making, eye to eye, soul to soul.

One evening after dinner together, I told him one of those things I wanted him to know. I wanted him to think about it, so he would live a little less hard on himself, a little softer, kinder, as he already was since we first met. "Levi, your desire to be strong is not a weakness. Rather it's something to build from and work with. Practice grace and kindness towards yourself each and every day. You don't have to fight against who you are but instead embrace it as one of the many exquisite layers of you that makes you so beautiful. Without it, you wouldn't be you. But to practice kindness and grace for yourself, you'll feel better within and later it will carry on to tame those thoughts of others too. I understand because I feel the need to be strong too and I know what much of it feels like."

He listened with eyes that held an openness I hadn't seen before. An openness that assured me my heart was heard. Our talks were as deep as ever, and open too. His walls of nerves and mine of uncertainty were gone. In place came a feeling of taking in every nuance of this new openness we shared with each other.

I had a chance to say to him those things I'd long thought and wished I could say, and it seemed he could too. He was softer, more open, easy. We were easy. We flowed together in a way that felt like a real life together. In a way that made a part of me not want to leave his side. But deep down I knew I had to. I had to walk my way because his love held strains neither of us could ignore. Binds that would only tighten when true reality began. We both knew it. But just for now, we were in love.

Life: Leaving

Finally, there came the time for me to go. As I was riding the drive to my new home, I messaged Levi when I would return. I told him that seeing him was a priority to me because I knew I would have needed to hear that too if I were him. His response was to call. He started our conversation a nervous schoolboy, endearingly so.

Of course, each time I would talk to him, there was a layer of walls that needed broken down. This time was no exception; he was nervous. Searching for words that would make the conversation flow, even though it did effortlessly on its own once he opened up. With every word of small talk that rarely passed between us, he told me he was anxious, or as he would rather put it, excited. But suddenly and with inexplicable candor, his beautiful heart opened up and shared itself fervently.

"I love you Allie. I Love you. When I say that I really mean it."

"I know you do. Just as I have the same love for you."

"I try to hide my feelings a lot. I'll daydream about you, about a life with you, and I push it away. Like aw she's gone. There's no sense in doing that. I say this time I'm going to be strong, I'm not going to let her in. But then I hear your voice. That's all it takes, and it's just like aw there it goes. Just having you near me, I feel you. You make everything better. You make me better. When I feel sad, when I'm low, I think it would be nice if she were here." I gripped the phone with both hands, breathlessly taking in this unexpected gift of words. His vulnerability made my heart catch. "I don't really want to be alone my whole life. I know I'd be alright. I would. But I don't want to be alone. I've thought of being with someone else. But then I think of you walking in, and I know that sick feeling I'd have, missing out on you, on everything. What I gave up. Everything is right and better when you're here. If there's one thing, this is real love. When I say I love you it's the real thing."

"And my love is with you always." I hoped he remembered these words in his low times.

"I love you. I'll always love you. Always." he said. There was a long pause when we both absorbed the words we just said to one another, and I knew our reverie had come to a lingering close.

We both spoke at once and chuckled. I let him talk. "Well Allie . . . I guess I'll get to my dinner."

"I hope I haven't kept you from it so long that it's burnt up!"

"Nawww, it'll be fine. Just fine."

"Well I hope it's a good one, and you enjoy a quiet, peaceful evening tonight."

"I hope you have a good evening too Allie, and sweet dreams to you . . . I'll be with you. I'll dream of you tonight."

"I'll be looking forward to seeing you in November."

"Yeah. We'll have to do something together. I'm not sure what. Or we could just be together here at the house. I'm sure we'll figure it out. I just can't wait to hold you in my arms."

If I could ever sink into a set of words and rest there, those would be it. I could feel his arms around me, I could smell his earthy, musky scent. Sense his depthful wonder. Feel his tender, livening touch. With that simple, powerful statement, he took me there. We didn't need words for that togetherness. Love didn't need words.

We exchanged two more I love yous and hung up the phone. Our love was but this reality between us we were pretending was tangible. More and more, it was fading into the truth that it was not. Neither of us were ready to face it just yet because, for now, it was too good to let go.

In the days that followed, reality settled in once again as my wiser voice of reason consoled my aching heart. I knew in his lack of contact, he was pushing it away too. It's what we had to do, each for our own reasons.

One thing I'd noticed about Levi was that when he really wanted something in life, he placed a glass ceiling right over the threshold of getting it. I'd heard and seen it happen time and time again. My mind had wondered if that instinctual part of him would apply to me someday, but my heart wouldn't listen to my mind. He was worth the risk. And oh how he was worth it. But it was true. That glass ceiling stood between us. His quiet was an expression of that nature.

Looking back, I wonder if that was the defining difference between us. I went after what I wanted. I desired to take risks in spite of fear. Because it's the only way you truly live. I'd hoped with growing worth, he'd live more fully too. I knew he wanted that. And it hurt to see that his glass ceiling would contain him in his struggle until he did. It's only we who can release ourselves from our own confines when we're truly ready.

Reflection: Letting Go

It felt like the rains of change had poured upon us without ceasing those months. I went for a walk, picking up acorns along my way. But as I held the varying shades of acorns between my fingers, I realized that the rain was exactly the thing that had drawn out their beauty. Just like when it touched the stones on the beach. Some look as common as a rock until a drop of water meets their surface, bringing a rich splash of color you may have never known was there before.

Many of the richest colors in our world come in the form of loss, and with loss comes the natural shed of tears. Tears are a human need, a release of pain, an expression of love, sometimes all integrated at once. They allow the ties that bind us, good or not, to let go. Only then can our richest colors within shine forth. There are pivotal times in our lives in which change rains pain that strikes to the core of us. It allows the measure of your beauty to meet the depth of your spirit so the world, if you let it, can see you too.

Painful as it was, that's what our rain was doing for me. It gave me a new definition of loving. It opened my eyes to what true love is, what it can do. And ultimately, dare I say, what it could do for me if I let it. Because like all things in life, love is a choice we make each and every day. It feeds us, it fuels us, it shows us the way. Giving and allowing it in are equally important in measure and mirth. Some forms of loss require us to ask ourselves what and who fuel us? What might we need to lose in order to gain?

Life: **Power of Unconditionals**

I knew him better than he knew himself. And isn't that an essence of love?

I believe there are capacities of the human heart that can only be accessed by unconditional love. No matter if that unconditional love is met unrequited or unaccepted, love comes for a reason. For the matter is, those souls not ready to receive or give back are perhaps the ones who need to greet unconditional love for the first time. What it feels like, looks like, how to trust it, know it, and welcome it in. In essence, it's the taming of a beast within, a beast created by a harsh outside world brought inward, that can be rightly healed from the inside and brought outward.

It's certainly not the job of a lover, but perhaps a calling so that two can understand love more together. Have a teacher, a preacher, *for a time.* Unconditional love is needed by us all. Isn't it?

Life: Someday

Someday is a haunting word. It plays across the mind and teases memories into the future. It plays tricks with your resolve and draws you to a place your mind knows you should not go but your heart leads you to anyway because of it. Your heart carries *someday* with an impish, hopeless, self-deprecating smile. If a heart were to be personified, of course. This was what mine did once we got to Michigan.

I'd think back on his words. "It's hard when you leave and come back. I miss you. It hurts. And I tell myself you've got to stop. You've got to push it out. So, I go and work out and for a while I don't think about you, I don't feel. And I guess it sort of feels good. Ya know, that pumping through me, I feel strong. But then, it always comes back. Time eventually lets me think about every day. I forget what this feels like when you go. What it is. It's happy. I'm happy when you're here with me."

There were days I felt weak in a way that made me worry for his sake. I'd wonder things, like 'Do you think a person remembers when you tell them you love them always? Sometimes I'd worry that he didn't. That he'd push me so far out of his mind that he wouldn't feel my love anymore. I wanted him to feel loved. Always. He said it was better when I was around. I knew that was true because he was better. Softer. More at peace. Happy. He said those things to me, but I saw them too.

Hearing the lack of happiness in his life alone made me sad. I related to him and the pain he went through. The feeling naturally came along with our come and go friendship. The unsustainability of it. I couldn't believe he'd remained close to me this long. I thought he'd have receded long ago to his safe place, alone. The question that pervaded both our minds as time passed between us was this. Is alone and safe enough anymore? Is safely alone as good as boldly happy? For me, I knew the former was never enough. I wanted the latter. I wanted more than this.

I wanted to be angry. We could have had that beautiful life together. He just wasn't able to take the leap for me any more than he could for himself through the years. But anger didn't come. All I could feel was sad. I knew this was his nature. I also knew if we were together, I'd live a life inside his fragile box of safe, in keeping his frustration down, when it came down to it. He had anxiety, and it wasn't something he treated in a healthy way. It confined his way of living and would someday restrict ours. It played with his mind and could someday meddle in our relationship. It kept him from fully giving me his heart, and for that, he couldn't fully receive mine. I knew how to assuage his senses, to reach through to *him*. But. When you love someone, it's important to consider the life you would share with them. Was this picture the life I wanted beyond the man? It wasn't in my power to change his anxiety, and it wasn't my journey to judge him living with it. What was my decision was whether his life's restrictions would become my own. If I went back to my home-town to be with Levi, if I changed my life to fit into his carefully built world, if I tended and took care of his mind and his heart, would I be happy? Would I be me? Would I truly live?

Those aren't always the things you think about when you're missing someone. I'd think about the special way that he made me feel, like magic. I didn't think about the classic way he fit my type, unstable, maybe just a little bit crazy, with the illusion of all the potential in the world. Intense. I didn't think about the way I set aside that unsettling feel of danger that came over me once in a while that was all so familiar. Needing me to break his walls down. We're all our own kind of crazy in big or small ways, it depends on the directions we drive ourselves. Potential is a tricky thing. For its power rests in the hands of its beholder, no matter what I may envision. This was a hard lesson I'd needed to learn a few times over.

I knew I could spend the rest of my life trying to figure him out, churning and reaching until my mind had room for nothing else but him. He felt like an even blend of home. Someone who saw all of me, deeply, loved me tenderly and also someone who was set at a neutral state of angry, unreachable, unsettling. Maybe that was part of the appeal. But I had a new home now. And it felt entirely different from my home before.

His eyes were like looking into the night sky, and I kid you not, they gave me the very same feeling. How could I give that up? But I must. I knew I must. To choose the life that came with him would be to choose a different shade of the same colored life that I had lived before. One that darkened those stars and dimmed the light in my eyes until it would be gone. Until we'd be gone. Perhaps this reasoning was true, or, by some chance for peace, perhaps I was simply telling myself this story so that I would allow myself to let go. And let go. And let go of him. And he of me.

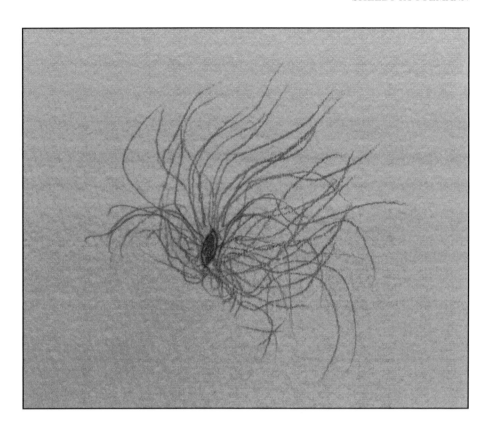

Reflection: Cottonwood

A plough of white softness from the cottonwood tree floated through the air like a cloud of drifting snow lost in time. I reached out to touch one and caught it in my hand, pulling it close to see. In a moment, it flew from my fingers on a breeze, before I was ready to part from its softness. Sometimes, accepting beauty into our lives entails the promise of letting it go just the same, in its own time, with a cottonwood measure of grace.

Life: Truth

The truth is the most powerful place we can rest in. Truth with ourselves. Truth with others. It really does set us free. It sets us free to feel our real feelings. Sets us free to take hold of the life we're meant to live.

Truth has held a lot of power in my life. The strength to face the truth, live in the truth, and finally accept the truth with mercy and grace can transform your life. These actions have gifts that only experiencing them yourself can unfold in your heart. Just as they did in mine.

With sadness yet respect at my own truth, and an understanding of the reasons for the seasons we live, I knew Levi was not my one. When I faced that truth, my hope fell, all the hope and love I'd placed in him became an ache, a disappointed desire. It was the loss of a dream I'd formed with him. And the loss of that untouchable dream made me fall down inside. I fell down in a secret way no one saw or heard.

Sometimes we avoid truths because they hurt to see fully, ache to act on, and take time to accept. Whether it be the truth of my dad or the truth of Levi or the truth of me, I had to be willing to let them exist and even more powerfully, let myself go from the hope and desire to make them different. Until I did that, I would stagnate my heart and my life in cycles that all had the same unsung end.

Do you ever have an ache for a love so deep you feel there's no time and no place, no member which can be an outlet for this love? One of the truths that I felt deep in my bones was that I had not met *him* yet: the kind of man I'd been waiting for. Somehow, facing the truth that Levi was not this man made me ache because I was losing faith that he'd arrive someday. I was losing faith that my dream I felt in my bones was real. The hole filled with a deep sense of loneliness in this world that became a part of me. But still, I waited and willed that he was out there, and I vowed I would be alone until I found *him*.

Reflection: **Raindrops**

In the forest, it rains. But not all the water hits the ground at once. Some of it lingers in the leaves till morning. It waits to fall until the rays of the sun hit the morning dew. And then it's as if the weight of the world is unleashed from each branch. A gentle shower cascading down in a cacophony of water and air, the sound of a rainstorm on a sunny day.

Just like the aftermath of an inner storm. The raindrops sometimes wait to fall in their own appropriate time. When the sun is shining. When warmth from a new day touches it. When the world doesn't know where it's coming from. But the trees are releasing the cleansing weight of the world to shower the earth below with a bath of nourishing drops to grow from.

This kind of morning was the season of life I was in. Listening to the sound of those branches in the breeze, I understood this was another way of living. Emotional release. Best done from the soul.

Reflection: Autumn's Release

A fresh mind in the morning looks at yesterday's problems and prayers with new eyes and answers. Because the time when you wake up from sleeping is one when you're closest to your spirit; you're still listening.

As I stepped out into the morning dew, I saw with clearer eyes. I felt with a renewed tenderness that welcomed me with a long-missed part of myself, peace.

Trees show us how to let go. As they cascade down, all the colors and shapes of leaves show just how many ways there are to let go. Some falling leaves catch your eye for they are special; they're different colors only God can make. Even since yesterday, leaves sprinkled across the ground had grown not just in number but diversity. Their different shapes and colors marked each tree's letting go of its own year of fighting for life and strength and light. Each was ready for a long, dormant rest, a faithful wait for renewal, new growth reaching farther and taller than yet before.

I stopped in my tracks and stared. A fallen tree rested in its place, roots splayed out and interwoven as if they never left the ground, yet connecting the earth and the sky, perfectly vertical. They'd become black as night. A color that most often brings to mind death, like the decay that was happening inside it. But as I took another step, I saw a tree that had lain there much longer than I thought. It sprang forth new growth, and I realized that in it grew a truth: In order for the growth of something new to begin, there must be the death of something that's lived its course. We learn when we're young that decay places nutrients into the soil to grow new life. But that's a lot like the processing of an ended relationship; those lessons and gratitudes fuel and enrich the soil of the heart for fresh, new relationships to brightly grow from in new forms. It's a transmutation of sorts that's cultivated in the human heart by love.

Reflection: Swans and Ducks

As winter began, a new pair of visitors frequented our waters. Trumpeter swans. Equal in grace and refinement, the duo were never far apart, always awe-striking. We were summoned to the window to take in their presence, watching their long necks glide into the water for breakfast.

One of Mom's and my favorite movie scenes comes from a film called *Love Affair*, when a very old Katherine Hepburn explains to Annette Benning the difference between ducks and swans. Her grandson, Warren Beatty, thought he was a duck; a common man dating around like a duck, never settling with one woman or truly sharing his heart. What he didn't see was that his restless heart came from the truth he'd yet to realize: that he was a monogamous, elegant, soulful swan of a soul. He hadn't yet found his match. It took finding an equal heart to unfold the depths inside himself.

The magic and devotion that cast across the water between these two birds on the lake before me made this favorite film scene come to life in a new way. And the rolls and rolls of circles that their rhythmic rocking sent out into the glassy water made me wonder if that swan kind of love has a ripple effect on us all.

Life: Where

In all my solitary healing time out in those woods and the breeze that stilled my spirit, I understood better where my heart was. Nature gives us these inner gifts when we seek it and allow it to heal us. Amongst nature, I found a reflected vision and understanding of love in all its expansive depths.

Love is found in the sparkling periwinkle eyes of a white-haired woman. The teasing swerve of an old tan truck. The heartfelt hug of a father lost but never gone. The cable man whose tires squealed into reverse when he saw me out on my evening walk. Or my electrician who'd tease a drop-in visit into his schedule to share a slice of pie or a dance. The answered prayer. A sunset on a fall day so full of color that it moves the soul. The first steps of a newborn fawn discovered on a dewy morning run. All of these moments are love. All of these things are Godspeak.

In these intimate moments with nature, I know I am Loved. In the meaning of my relationships, I know I matter. It's my hope that through my story you know you are Loved too and that Love is only a prayer away, a step into the woods, the following of your heart. If any of my words could reach across this page, I hope that my love for you, dear reader and friend, is felt because sharing my story is an act of love for you. And I know that if I knew you personally, if you saw yourself through my eyes, you'd see a beautiful, poignant person fit to be painted across these pages too. Everyone is deserving of love and is a one-of-a-kind embodiment of it.

Life: Real Dreams Meet Daydreams

I had made my resolve. I knew what was best. I was moving on. But I still thought about him. I still felt the love that doesn't go away when these decisions are made. So, I found myself day-dreaming at times.

Sometimes I wondered if in another lifetime he had courage and I had no fear. In that lifetime, we sang when we did the dishes. He played his guitar on our porch steps as we sang the sun down. He chopped wood and I tended the sunflowers. He worked our garden while I worked our home, and as our family grew, so did our love. He held me in that way he's done real tight, when I have to take a breath to take it all in. And I know this is it. We know, because we do.

But our dream was just a place I visited for a while. And those cane poles resting by the stump Levi cut for us down at the river that flowed by our wooden house, waited for me to visit when I missed him. When I wanted to see his bright eyes as his whole face lit up whenever he saw me. The blush in his cheeks as we'd cook side by side, him fumbling for words and throwing up his hands. Dancing slow, nose-to-nose in reverie, losing track of time. The beautiful flowers that only he could choose, though half the time I think he stole them.

There's a difference between daydreams and real dreams. Daydreams are fanciful, and you imagine them creatively. You keep them in your pocket to look at for a smile. Real dreams are powerful. Real dreams hold fast in your spirit. You know deep down that you cannot fully live your life without realizing them. They're something you can't deny because they're a part of your-self. The key is to know and recognize that difference, especially when you're faced with the choice between them. For me, there was no choice at all, only a strong set of heartstrings to that pocket full of daydreams that ached as I firmly set out toward my soul's dream instead.

As with most all big choices we make, there comes a time when they are challenged.

Life: A Return

There's something about losing someone precious to you at a time when you're climbing through other losses that wreaks havoc on your heart. It pulls you down deeper into a cavernous hole of heartbreak and seeps into the heart with a questioning will for the light. My uncle called at midnight. "Mom's dead." were all his words. We screamed. To her home we went. The house was to be sold. We needed time to say goodbye to the memories.

Once there, it was already a shell of what their lives had been, Grandma and Papa's. Their belongings disassembled and taken away, it felt as if the spirit of home was absent, and instead stood simply a house. It made this comforting place not anymore. But still. We needed it. Her. The both of them. Sorrow runs as deep as love. But after time, the sorrow of this loss fades into the grateful comfort of sensing their presence beyond all veils. Because love traverses all.

In the midst of family memories and visits and time in the shell of a life we were leaving behind, I needed closure with Levi. The past was too close to the present that I had just barely let go of. I needed to be sure.

As I walked up to the white screen door, my mind traced back to other nights. I knocked on his door. He opened it and softened, his smile loving and aching at once. We stepped into his kitchen and stood there in the glow of his cabinet's colored Christmas lights that stayed there year-round and talked for a moment, but mostly there was silence, softness, knowing. I couldn't sit tonight. I came for a reason, and I had to stay true to it. Drawn by the warm glow emanating from his living room, I stepped toward it.

A tall, narrow tree glowed in the corner, only adorned with glowing white lights. Both of us fond of that romantic softness. I stepped over to it to touch its branches. "I love your Christmas tree. It's perfect." I said sincerely. When I looked back at him, what I saw was the purest open light of happiness and love I had ever seen in Levi. It poured from his eyes all the way through his whole face as he looked back at me. I took a mental picture of that moment, to keep with me.

I had to tell him all the things I wanted him to hold onto within him, make my love heal inside him far beyond all of these moments together as I had done so many times before and he'd unknowingly done for me. Cupping his face, I looked at him again. He couldn't meet my gaze. Sometimes I think he couldn't handle the intensity of our eyes meeting. At this moment, I think it was the sadness in the truth of love and goodbye. "You deserve the world."

"Yeah." He smiled soaking in the meaning of those words. "You deserve the moon." He wrapped his arms around my waist and swayed me slowly in the dark of his kitchen. Silent. Knowing.

The sadness in his eyes reflected the loneliness in my own. It scared me. Like looking into a part of myself I feared to face. I kissed his lonely face and held him, knowing that those kisses wouldn't take it away forever. Knowing I'd seen into those windows to the soul beyond his walls.

"I couldn't ask you to make that choice." I ventured. I had to.

"I know, but I could. I need to." Did he mean it?

We had talked about our dreams of life together, but talking about dreams wasn't enough anymore. I wanted reality. I wanted commitment. I wanted him to take me in his arms and not be able to let go. To love me so strong that letting go wasn't an option. This was what I had come to find out. I had to show him how much I loved him because if I didn't, I would never know. I'd never know what would have happened if I had. Someone like him needed reaffirmed, loved a little more. I readily poured it out to him. I felt like if there ever was a moment when we could meet each other at a common place, it could be this one, but somewhere within, I knew the truth. When I looked at his face again, his whole body sighed.

"What is it?" I asked gently.

"I miss you."

I miss you. Said it all. All the dreaming. Daydreaming. The realities we had figured out, it was all a fantasy that would never be. It was time to let him go, as heart-wrenching as that process would be. Move on with my life. But for now, I set all those cascading thoughts aside and just enjoyed this moment with him. It would be my last, and I wasn't going to waste it on hurt feelings. He was too important to me. That was far bigger than feelings. With those words, *I miss you*, my heart had fallen down in a quiet, familiar way that letting go ensued, a feeling I knew well enough to keep from this moment.

I treasured our last kisses. Without question, he walked me to my car.

"Someday, we'll be together." He nodded with a firm conviction that didn't match his voice or his eyes, even in the darkness. I simply read his face in reply.

"I wonder if they have polar plunges in Michigan."

"They cancelled them due to risk of life." I said ironically not joking. "But if they did, you'd be champ. You train for those things. With your cold showers. You crazy person!"

"Yeah. That's what I was thinkin'. That'd be nice."

I shook my head at his boyish grin. The spark of affection in my eyes sent his bashful ones up to the stars with a shiver.

I opened the car door and turned to face him, forcing myself to do what had to be done, yet taking in the moment for what it was worth. Because it was worth so very much to me. Something inside of me felt that this would be the last time I saw him. I pushed it down so I could be with him truly, not fall apart. For the first time, the joyfulness in his eyes told me he didn't have the same knowing as me.

"I love you Allie."

"I love you too Levi."

After one more hug, he stepped away. I knew he'd watch me go till I was out of sight. He always did. Those countless moments played across my mind as I drove away, waving gently with the window down.

Walking to the school door when he dropped me off at lunch, his little blue truck just crawling away, his small handsome face in the rearview mirror capturing every moment of me like a picture in a frame. Treasuring me. Him standing in his driveway late at night no matter how cold or how dark, watching till my car was out of sight, lifting a hand when I did mine. Now the image of him standing in the snow was etched into my mind's eye. The snowflake Christmas light glowing in his window casting its warmth upon the snow. His heart and his joy on this night still a beat away.

I had needed to come here tonight for myself. For him. His words, I realized, gave me the answer that had whispered in my bones.

Levi didn't try often. I always knew that. But it was the person within him that I loved. In this pivotal time, I saw more clearly how big the little things were. I'd made many excuses for their absence, and could last for a lifetime. I'd fought to reach his heart within, and that could never cease. But perhaps my stamina would. Perhaps all this had been a fast-forward to show me the truth of things.

Reflection: Vision

Sometimes, I had visions of myself, my spirit, making it to shore. On the other side of this ocean of pain and trial, only to be so weak I could barely pull myself from it to see the island of my dreams before me. The one I'd spent a lifetime reaching without knowing. Lived for, yet died inside, to reach. As we were making our way there, that was the fear and the feeling that took root inside of me. And as pain found its footings in places I hadn't known before, I could only hope to restore the faith I once had. It had come so much easier before. I thought of all the dreams I'd been given, and yet the reality of them was becoming a part of my pains too. Did that define an ungrateful heart? I hoped not. I thanked God with conviction for where we were today. I just didn't feel joy anymore. There were walls there, like the joy I once carried on my sleeve was the inner layer of a Russian doll. My sadness was the shell on the outside, so easily touched. My layers rearranged. I felt myself and like a foreigner to me all the same. All this lies beneath the surface of a same but different me.

Life: Fog Clearing

We'd returned to town, and of course, I visited my father. It was the right thing to do. I sat in his new living room conversing with him about his new life, the same yet different, his intimidating tension was painfully familiar. Terse small talk turned to serious conversation.

"I never wanted you." "I never wanted you." Each time he said it, more passivity and force came with it somehow at once. I couldn't tell if he was goading me or if he really meant it. All the times he'd said that rang like the echo of a bell in my chest until he said it again. I finally had the courage to speak for myself.

"You know, as a child I was perceptive. I knew you didn't want me. I could feel that."

Legs splayed out in his straight-backed chair, he paused. He hadn't expected me to say that. "Well, you have to understand, I'd already been divorced once and was paying child support on them. If this marriage didn't work out, I'd have another to pay out."

Through the sting, I chose to see that as his way of telling me it was the circumstances, not me. Conversation shifted again.

"I've been an atheist for over thirty years. I've studied the top atheists of the time of World War Two. We didn't go to church when you were growing up. What was it that made you have faith?" He looked at me with truly questioning eyes.

Something inside of me wanted my answer to be just right, as if my answer could either support or fracture the forming of my father's faith. So, I spoke as openly as I could. "Mom taught me to pray when I was a little girl. She taught me how to have faith. When I was in my first relationship and things weren't good, I remembered how she showed me to pray in hard times. So, I did. I prayed for direction for months, and God helped me. I could feel his guidance in my heart. And when I felt drawn to go to church, mom supported me, suggesting our cousin's. Yuvonne made such a great impact on me, and she needed me too. That's how God works. From there, He has shaped the pathway of my life, and I turn to God in many ways. I have a personal relationship that means very much to me. God is an unending source of unconditional guidance and love. I wouldn't be where I am today without my faith. I believe faith, sometimes, comes unto you at the right time, perhaps from God reaching out to us through people and things."

"Well, that Bible study you started me at was where they really prayed for you and prayed for people that needed something. I didn't care for that workbook, though."

"I'm glad it's something you've enjoyed. I hoped that for you." I replied.

His demeanor shifted at my compassion, even his body. "I'm sorry I wasn't the father I should have been, made you feel wanted. I'm glad your mother made you feel wanted." He twisted and cast his face to the side like a child being forced by their teacher after recess, but he said it, nonetheless. And no one was forcing him.

I didn't know what to think, so I just took him in. I didn't say it was okay. Maybe in some facet of his being, God was able to access him. That's the healing power of knowing God. If what he said to me was true, the moments he spent in prayer with God gave him a peace he hadn't known. For that, I was glad we'd walked this path. It had been purposeful, worthwhile in the end.

That didn't mean his former self was erased. His more ominous intensity still flared much. I was still trying to instill calm, positivity, and grace. The visit made me realize two very important things: I was treading on the ice of long ago, long before me. And yet through this journey, my father, my mother, and I, each still connected by our experiences, we all had our feet firmly on the pathway of the life we were destined to reach.

Reflection: Winter Swirls

Looking out across the white field that was once a wavy lake, the rolling winds of snow spark the imagination. Something about their force. It feels like a herd of wild horses could surge right out of the plumes of rising snow into clear line of sight, bringing a deep breath of energy from toe to head. They weave around you and encompass you in a single stilling moment, every hoofbeat drumming in your ears. You take in their musky scent, the stirred-up dust that catches in their coat. The moment fills you. In that single moment, you're overcome with their drive and togetherness and you carry it with you like a gift. Honored with an awe in knowing a force like this exists. And you get to experience it.

That's what I see when I look out upon the drifting winds of our wintery lake. The rolling, twisting, whipping, curling snow drifts blow through the skyline, one towering billow after another. Each snowflake, riding in the wind across the course it blows. Every ice crystal shifting in sync. Like a sandstorm, a raging drift of fog upon a dreamy morning's dew. When we pause to watch it out our snug winter's window after a drifted driveway of snow has been moved, we appreciate the power of this force. To shift the wintry sands beneath our feet. After the foundations of our lifelines seem to slip, sometimes the dunes of winter snow that rest when nature's calmed place us in a new world grant a different view of our landscape than before the storm. And we realize that the ferocity of storms, the might of their winds are just the power we need to whip old comforts out from under us and replace them with a new sense. A lens we'd ne'er earned were it not for having weathered the storm.

Knowing that storms come in life to refine our circles, renew our foundations, strengthen us, helps us take in the beauty of the details. Gusts' ability to change course in the snap of a moment, the beauty of every billow as it floats its majestic way across the lake and settles somewhere onto its piling destination. The forces of nature are unbridled and ever-changing. Their might strikes awe, especially when we pause to feel them working their force in our lives, honor how lucky we are to experience and be a part of something bigger, stronger, mighty, taking hand and saying this is the way. Waking up the next morning, in an instant, or perhaps slowly to that new world whirled just for you.

This is how it felt clearing out our lives one piece at a time. Unreal, shocking, heart wrenching, awe-inspiring, like losing and gaining a part of yourself at once. Knowing all the while that these moments in time were a whirlwind driving with a force of the universe, a force of God, a force of us, that was greater than what we ever thought possible. One that let the heart free.

Life: **Fog into Truth**

Pain struck deeply when he told me he never wanted me. But simultaneously, there was a release from that pain. Because for the first time, I understood why I wasn't wanted. More importantly, I understood when I wasn't wanted. It had nothing to do with me or who I was. It wasn't that I wasn't enough or something I did. It wasn't some unfathomable thing I had yet to figure out. He simply did not want me before I ever was conceived. And for that, I was released from a lifetime of feeling like the leper kid. The one who was rejected, unwanted for *who she was*. Whose love was never *enough* to love. For the first time, I could *let go*.

With these words, he had given me the power to make my own choice. To release myself from the confines of my history, my thoughts, my constricted heart around the puzzles of walls and defeat.

I can't even remember the rest of our conversation, but I left his place in a daze. Thinking yet not having a thought at all, just feeling a clarity I hadn't ever remembered. A clarity that was me.

Now my visits with him weren't all this profound. The next time I came, he was irate. Ranting about the government, work, family, even threatening me. There came a point when I felt cornered by him with no real way out. I feared I may not ever leave.

That's when I realized that though I had forgiven my father, I had to have compassion for myself as well. *Compassion breeds forgiveness.* I had to forgive myself of the sins I'd taken on for others' sakes. In turn, the sins I'd collected against myself. It was time to honor the being that was me. I mattered too. It was a matter of spiritual survival.

I needed to not forget who he was. I needed boundaries, which began at not being alone with him again. As all this dawned on me, I knew that there were words I needed to say to him. I had to because

I would have no other opportunity to say them to his face without an audience, and words this personal need to be said alone.

His eyes looked as if they were coming off a high from the exaltation of power he threw over me in the threats and lashings of fear and hate that at this point in writing my story, I don't care to repeat nor revisit. But, as I stepped onto the threshold of the door, those eyes would not meet mine. Instead, they cast anywhere but into my own.

"Dad," I said.

"Yeah, what?"

"Our relationship has been difficult for me through the years. I have seen things for what they were. I felt it all. Dad . . . I love you, and I forgive you."

His head shot up, eyes meeting mine with a moment of sheer vulnerability that I'd never seen in this man. And in that moment, I saw that deep down in his soul, he knew what all he'd done was wrong. He carried it all. It was a piece to the inner puzzle of his troubled soul. And in that moment, I hoped my forgiveness could release some of those troubled pieces for him. Because I did love my father. Unconditionally.

"Thank you, Allie. I love you." He gave me a hug. A hug that pressed, that lasted a beat longer, a hug with energy in it, like an exchange of love that could only be called a truce. A moment between us that I knew was once in a lifetime.

I walked to my car and drove to my childhood home. Now lit with the Christmas lights of its new family, I parked out of view behind the little pine tree where I used to jump in fall leaf piles. I watched the lights twinkle in the darkness of the winter night. And I knew it was over. I had done what I needed to do for us all. And I cried for all the power and pain that it'd been.

Reflection: Hearts Grow

I used to love looking out onto the field beside my home. The tendrils and boughs of grass soothe my spirit as I soak in the view. And in the winter, when their brown stalks and fuzzy blossoms are nested in a fresh blanket of snow, there's a sense of romantic peace in watching them slowly sway in the cold north breeze.

Then one day, a man came in on large equipment with a force much like that breeze. In that day, he eradicated the field of wildflowers and tall grasses I'd come to love so. Gone was a peaceful place.

The man nor the owner who directed him couldn't know how special their place was just naturally. As it's told, beauty, and also worth, is in the eye of the beholder.

Over a year went by. I looked out on that field, first with disappointment, but then in interest. I was watching a transformation take place. Nature was taking it back. Another well-known truth of our world. Yet it spoke another truth to me because I was walking the same path as that field. Rebuilding.

There are times in our lives when a man or a woman or a thing comes in. Invades and destructs the pure beauty and peace that once was. Reasons vary. To dwell on why is a drain and a waste. Sometimes, like the field, worth is not aptly seen. In other cases, it's sheer chance.

But I don't believe in coincidence. I believe in synchronicity. I believe in opportunity. And with every challenge comes the choice to find one. When we face times of destruction in our lives, we are met equally with challenge. Ready or not, someone above believes we are.

When we choose to dwell, we stay in that challenge, that destruction, for a lifetime. When we make the choice to take the path to rebuild or in any case, like the field, regrow, we lift ourselves from the soil anew. The same yet different.

Regrowing is not starting over, mind you. For if you remember the field, you know it regrew once its bearings had changed. That makes it stronger, wiser, the same yet reformed. Like us, the field adapts.

When we choose to regrow, we rise up from changed soil with new nutrients for success. New sensitivities, strengths, awarenesses, that before were yet unknown. When we rise again, we are as beautiful and peaceful as we've ever been. Only this time, we're refined, a new edition, better fit for our world.

In this sense, could it be said that destruction is a gift? Maybe not. But it is necessary for us to transform the greatest parts of ourselves. Because without it, how would our hearts grow?

Reflection: Rose Sunset

The light reflecting on the lake called me to look up at the sky. Hues of rose and violet played upon the glassy contours of the chopping waves. I stepped to the window and gazed above. Calming rolls of blue and violet rolled across and blanketed the evening sky as if to cool and calm, touch the spirit with our eyes with beauty before we go to sleep. But there was meaning to this view.

The veil of the blue evening clouds had parted and thinned to reveal a pink softness that lies beyond. On a plane much higher than those cool and quiet clouds, was a light of love. That pink radiated with a hue that spoke of softness, kindness, radiance that come in the gentlest of ways. But the message that called the strongest in this sunset was this: That rose-lit opening to the clear setting sky came and it went. It spoke of the opportunities we are given in love. We must be open to them when they call upon our door. Unexpected or not, we must be prepared to say yes to love when it calls.

Time can be spent in awe of the rolling clouds without ever knowing the majesty of an opening to the purity of true love. Likewise, that opening can be observed in reserve, a stillness that, by default, says no. When an opening, an opportunity comes in our lives, we must have the open spirit within ourselves with which to meet it. And we must have the courage and grace to know to take the call. For the betterment of ourselves and ultimately the world. Because when we receive true love, we give it. A fusion that makes anything possible.

Is this real or pretend? Deep down, I knew it must be real for my father to grant me such a gift and passage of words so acutely directed at my heart. The question the universe was asking me was, *Are you willing to accept this gift of your father's love?*

You see, love, the love we seek, comes in a multitude of forms. For every person has a kaleidoscope of colors in their heart that are expressed in the most complex of ways. So often we seek to see the colors and shapes, expressions, of love we prefer out of sheer stubborn will. Sometimes, we search for the ways of loving that we feel missing in our lives in order to feel loved by another and miss the image of love right in front of us entirely, never knowing it was there all along. Never appreciating the incandescence of the kaleidoscope within the human heart. But love isn't given on demand. It is as intricate as this antiquated toy yet simply innate.

Every human has within them the truths of love. That's why abuse does damage. Because every being knows what love is. How it feels and looks and is given. It's natural because we are children of God. And God is inside of us, innately. But once the world comes into our way, in comes fear, uncertainty, into our hearts. Our minds play tricks that tell us we are unworthy, undeserving, that walls must be built, and masks must be worn, even as if thine own skin. And by the time all those untruths become interwoven into a person's idea of themselves, their idea of love becomes entangled with those untruths. In life, things beget one another, just as pure love begets pure love. One must love themself to love another.

I believe that the way a person loves themself is a language with which they speak their love to those they hold most dear. We can see this illustrated all around us. My best friend feels himself unworthy. So, his dearest ones must prove their worth to him time and time again to earn his trust, his time, his day. It makes them feel how he feels, not because he wants their heart to fall as low as his, but because he is unaware. Unaware of his worth. Unaware that he begets abuse.

And is it not love to cast illusions equal to those in which you live? For my dad to love another through desperate flares of hatred and jealousy from the inadequate feeling that lies within? To have passing glimmers of vulnerability and care? Maybe to make another feel as lost and hurt and confused as you do is not malign but rather it's a reflection of the reality he lives in. Isn't love a sharing of one's heart? That doesn't guarantee that what's in a heart is healthy and held by oneself. Love is not a subscribed notion. It's not our place to define it or deny its presence because it's spoken in the only ways we each know how to live and love ourselves.

It's our job to accept that every person comes into this world with an innate sense of love but comes through this world with an altered perception of it. The language their heart speaks, the language it hears in, and that makes it unique. One's love can only be understood by a determined understanding of the person.

The same could be said for my father and his illusionary mask. For those who want his love, the illusion of camaraderie draws them near. The illusion of a threat makes them feel unsafe. The illusion of need makes them feel valued. The illusion of being discarded makes them feel worthless. The illusion of hate makes them feel hated. And by the time you get to the illusion of care, they feel just as unsafe as if it were that threat. All of this illusion I'd chosen to remain in because I was seeking love. All of us seek love from our core family, but sometimes that creates a great imbalance of power. The power of illusion takes away from the innocent the ability and stability to love thyself. Generationally.

Instead, self-love becomes beaten, shattered, scattered, and as elusive as the model itself because how you love yourself is turned grey by all these illusions.

Perhaps my father's love was elusive, most of all toward people with personal power, because the anchors in his life were unable to give him stable, constant love. Maybe they instead took his power of love without giving it back openly in return. Maybe that inconsistency, that sense of unrequitedness, held power over his spirit that he could not get out from under. Maybe it trained the way he loved himself, and it changed the way he could love another. Maybe his parents carried trials and traumas of their own in their hearts that made them unreachable. My father's love was just as unreachable, disempowering, fearsome. My father's love makes those who love him feel unreached, disempowered, and fearing in return. Maybe it was the perpetuation of a cycle.

Here lies the difference between perpetuators of a cycle and breakers to the chain. Here lies the choice: One can continue more of the same and live a life of resentment that festers into a demon inside. A demon that infiltrates the spirit with a poison and lurches out and commits the same crimes done unto him. Saint Augustine said that "resentment is like drinking a poison and waiting for the other person to die." What dies is every chance for love to enter the heart. Alongside every chance for love to be shared with those who deserve it most and want to give it to you and watch you grow. Together.

Here lies a choice to burst forth. Heal the inner wounds. Turn to love; to God. Face fears and pains head on and give them love because that's what they're truly crying for. Share in the journey that is you, highs and lows. Because embracing it all, embracing all the mountains and valleys that rest within your soul, that is the merit which allows you to be the kind of light to guide others back to shore.

It is our duty to cast off illusions, most of all our own. Fears, instabilities, walls, and defenses to reach our hearts with which we came into this world. Recognize where our innate concept of love shifted with someone else's story lens, casted a shadow of doubt upon our ray of light. Because until we do, we'll feel a dimming to our glow inside that only fades us more with time. And as we neglect our true selves, we become a link to the chain of the cycle. Break it! Be you! Shine bright! You have the *power*. Only you can do what you were called here to do. Today is the moment to begin anew. Somewhere, in this moment, far but near, I'm here, with you, smiling. You can do it too.

I still to this day do not know for certain the intent behind my father's gifted Bible. The child inside me questions how it's intended to manipulate. To her, this Bible was a symbol of the hard-won journey that made me a warrior for love, a test of trials that taught me how to be a beacon for those on weary roads. The hope-filled child, so in touch with that innate sense of all that true love is, she knows that Bible was a token of triumph. A testament that Love prevails to reach into hearts and souls. Love pierces through the veils of Earthly works. Love allows one soul to bring Heaven to another. So long as one practices the greatest measures that the heart can give: patience, compassion, forgiveness, and acceptance.

I keep that perfectly chosen, quoted Bible from an abusively loving man on my bookshelf. It brings color to the kaleidoscope that is my heart. It's a reminder to me that love can do *anything*. All miracles come from Love because God is Love.

Reflection: Waking Wonder

I was in a dream . . . I stepped over to a man my age slouched on a bench. His hair that reached down past his shoulders was the color of mine. He wore a blue and white pinstriped, buttoned shirt with a suede jacket over top. He was emotional, raw, and open. "I'll always remember the incredible person you've been to me. You tried to make me understand." he said.

I was confused at what his words meant but the depth beneath them stirred my heart just as deeply. Without thought, I knelt down and hugged him, wanting to relieve his fraught feelings, needing to show him he was loved.

Cradling the back of his head with my hand, I could feel that his hair was greasy. His face was shaven, but he was grubby up close. I worried whether the man took care of himself. By the sense of his words and his energy, I knew he was going away, and for some reason that made me sad. As I stayed in that embrace for a moment longer to comfort him, I felt his energy. In a waking jolt, I realized he was my father.

. . . Some dreams leave us compelled to *wonder* deeply.

Life: **My Choice**

When Dad and I talked, he often turned to me about things that he was wavering on. Decisions he had to make or thoughts he was unsure of. As if the respect rooted between us made me a safe place for him to land. Even though he tended to go his own way. And even though there were times I didn't know what to expect, times I felt abused like long ago, a part of me felt special that I could be that person for him. Because, Lord knows, I had reached for it with heart and soul! And I intended to continue to honor him and my mother by keeping reality between us. That meant life was going to be different than that of my life before. But this sense of hope and connection between my father and me was tainted with the past. I realized that I could never truly feel that he loved me, if he did, because I'd always be watching for the manipulations and revocations that had come before. I had finally achieved a semblance of what I'd long wanted with my dad, only to realize that it wasn't good for my heart or my mind.

I am always going to feel. I feel with my whole heart, at the very depths of me, and when I do it's like those feelings in my heart reach my soul. It is for that reason, I acknowledged how manipulation affects my heart so deeply. That the play with my emotions is not a game. Rather, it's a poison that keeps me awake at night, that even makes me question other relationships. It draws me in and casts me out, but I still hope, and so I hate myself for being a fool and yet I love myself for loving through, which keeps me there. So, in essence I end up as confused and unloving toward me as he. How toxic must that be?

I know how toxic it is. I know all too well. It's like a sickness that runs through my veins late at night when no one is there to see me not being happy, not being strong, not being the me that I know I am, but instead being the me that wrestles with muddied truths that have weighted my heart. Those muddied truths about myself, the unneeded pressures, settled into my heart and stayed there too long because I'd allowed it. I'd allowed myself to be abused in hope to be loved. I'd allowed myself to love unrequited until my self's love was unrequited too.

When you live in that space for too long, you begin to see the world through an isolated lens. I'm philosophical, I'm deep, I'm intuitive, I'm beautiful, but because of or in spite of all these things, because of or in spite of the isolation of manipulation, I feel that no one understands me. I'm unreachable. I wish and I wonder and I ache so deeply that I feel it in my cells, like an ache in my stomach that curls into my chest until I realize I'm not breathing but shallow fragments of breath. But I am left with a need. A need to know I am loved. A need to find that in love, reality, and truth. But the only way out of this isolating place was to understand that it wasn't just time to let go, it's time to move on. I needed to separate my life from my dad's.

It was time to let go of grey, uncertain love. It was time to recognize that I know what healthy love is and what it is not; that I always have. It's time that I not accept the latter for any reason. It's time that I respect my heart for its deep and whole entire worth. It's time that I honor the reality that I *live through my heart*. It's time that I not look back. Because looking back serves me no purpose but perpetuating abuse, but when I look back, I become my abuser because I'm keeping myself stuck there. Stuck in that space of yes and no, respected and degraded, trusted and questioned, thought of and lured, until my mind is a playground of uncertainty. It's sickening. I saw I had to let it go. This wasn't me. These inner landscapes were iterations of circumstances I needed to let go of, and until I could see that; until I could accept it; I'd hang onto the trap of manipulation that led me to abuse my own heart. With time, it would only get worse. I'd welcome people into my life that show me this hard lesson again and again, in this way and that, until I'd finally burst open my eyes to see. And what I'd see is myself. Tired, emptied, weary, but free.

Life: The Strength of Hurting

Have you ever felt like your soul could scream? Like all the hurts of loving the people in your life so unconditionally only to lose them surmount to meet and come together into one great warrior within you? One that comes to understand what *you* need? What you don't deserve? What you have to walk away from?

That's what made me scream inside. Each time I've walked away, I've had to cut out a gorgeous piece of loving another person that I've intertwined my heartstrings to. A beauty that I can't sustain because it just won't allow. And breaking that bound of love, it kills. It turns my insides out to see the patterns of goodbye. Each time I see the destruction that life's path would lead to, it's a grateful hurt. But that doesn't make the tearing of goodbye any less searing to my soul.

Yet these experiences taught me to have worth and love for myself, and they'd taught me that setting out to heal others caused me a great deal of heartache. I wasn't meant to ride someone else's journey alongside them. I needed to focus on my own path, uncomfortable as it was to live for myself. I needed to reach my own destination, though I didn't know yet where that would be, beyond this place up north.

This time, letting go created a strength from a different place. It created a dragon within me, a fierceness that rose up with the force to look farther, reaching past my feelings in my heart when I wanted to submit to myself and crumble into choosing my past. This time, I chose to simply love what this beauty taught me and reach for my future.

Reflection: **Pruning**

I kept feeling like God was pruning our tree. Like pruning off branches makes for new growth. Dead branches, even branches we wanted to hold onto. And through cutting all that off, we hurt and we stood still for a time because of it, just like a cold barren tree in winter. But after time, pruning makes for new growth. Things we never imagined and wouldn't have had we not experienced this extreme chapter. God was moving mountains through what we saw as pain. We were in the valley and only He knows what peak is in store. That's the faith I held onto and what I thank Him for.

Life, in its greatest trials, is a test of trust. I trust life in the face of disappointments, people in the face of piercing betrayals, and God because He is my Father. Loving me, knowing me better than I've ever known Him before. Like all things in life, trust is a choice. Sometimes, the greatest choice of all. I choose to trust my Father.

Life: **My Love's Worth**

I would tell myself until this truth felt possible . . . My love is worth sacrifice. I'm one of a kind, treasured, and adored. I'm worth the time and effort. My sincerity attracts the like. I am truly loved. Those who know me are proud of me. I'm someone unforgettable to care for for life and am by many. I make a lasting impression on people. Being around me lifts people up most times. I am adored. My heart and spirit surpass my beauty. My love and spirit fill people's hearts. All these things I must keep in my awareness for the resonance and the willpower of my worth is a determiner of my destiny.

Reflection: Transmutation

I wake from sleeping. In that slumber, I saw a woman in a flowing dress stand atop a hill. She blows out a breath on pursed lips and with it she empties her epiphany and sorrow and casts upon the world a lifetime of awakened dreams. I realize that woman is me. Renewed. The world loved by her in the deepest way her heart had left. Herself loved, purified, in the process.

It is on the greatest paths to discovery, we find the greatest mystery of all.

Reflection: Sadness

When I was young, I felt I had to silence my voice. I felt that I needed to make everyone comfortable in order to share love with them. But I learned that sacrificing my feelings didn't serve anyone, least of all me. I thought tolerance was a virtue, but I learned compassion held more power instead. I found that silence was the last thing this world needed. Instead, we need to honor the truths in our lives.

One of those truths I came to was that the soul inside every man needs a compassionate *voice* of *love*. A voice to come to them and recognize the qualities he beholds and the love he carries inside of him.

Our shadows of pain serve a purpose. Like the purpose of sadness is that it helps you process the things that plague you, most especially your heart. Without its pain, how would you know where to look for your sorrows? Pains shine a light on where to heal. They help man to grow. But the formation of shadows is also determined by the path one chooses when they meet the crossroads of adversity. One may fall far into the dark, away from love and into resentment, hate, or anxiety. Or they may reach high faithfully for the light and wisdom that burn effortlessly, enduringly, inside every soul.

For the depth of my heart's love, these depths reflect into equivocal despair when love morphs into loss. I had depths that used to scare me. Depths of a sorrow so deep I ached from the core of me... because I loved from my core. For years, I've feared the power of my own heart; the might of its love that makes a plummet from love to loss. That fear of myself has kept me running. Running from having a real love to last a lifetime because to risk it all I feared I'd lose my grip on joy. Running fearful only kept me at a distance from feeling the beat of my powerful heart, leaving me still emanating love yet dulled to accepting it by a slow burning ache that can only be healed by honoring and respecting myself. By turning toward my heart instead of away from it. By saying yes to my heart's dreams rather than keeping my heart on a leash. I needed to unleash my heart for the sake of its living and thriving. I needed to remove my fears, eradicate limitations; if I lived my love without holding myself in, it would surpass anything I imagine. Fear begets suffocation. Tenacity, that's what begets the courage to be all that you are.

Reflection: Effervescence

Snow. Layers upon layers of snow deepen over hills and valleys of the north-wooded earth, encasing its life in frozen time. One would think under all that weight of water and time, all of life would be smashed. Some of it is. Grasslands flatten. Ready to be composted into new. But other beings: moss, lichen, wintergreen, and prairie willow. They spring forth the moment the sun strikes them once again, as if the tests of time, and yes snow, never touched them. Glory be to the plants who bear weight while being weightless there's an effervescence to their springing that sings praise to us all. All whom rise to greet the day upon the lifting of mighty weights.

Reflection: Water

The sound of the wind in the tops of the trees feels like home all my own, personal to be shared with the chickadees that chatter joyfully behind me as I settle down in the moss by the stream.

Something about this stream captivates me. It makes me follow it up its way. The peat moss and the tree roots, the twigs and the needles soften my steps as the water trickles below. The twinkling leaves tell me that there are few left in this part of the forest come fall. Filled with sounds, smells, and rich colors of autumn, it feels like a different land. It's filled with meaning when you feel it closely.

I look down upon the current of the stream. It flowed unrelenting. Streams flow into brooks. Brooks run into creeks. Creeks into rivers, and rivers into ponds, bays, lakes. Ultimately, every waterway is flowing toward the largest, deepest body of water it's connected to. This stream would make its way into Lake Michigan. Science says the reason for this is that gravity draws water from its source toward the center of Earth. But I feel a human connection too. We are all like the streams and brooks that gather and flow into these larger bodies of water. Sometimes, the appearance of our surface betrays the reality of our tow. We support life in some. We can cause death in others. Sometimes we're transparent, others we're opaque, depending on what's been put into us and around us. When we meet an obstacle, we flow around it or create a gully of depth and dive deeper. Sometimes we rise, and sometimes we fall, but we all get where we're going as long as we remember water's key: keep flowing.

Life: Choice

We visited my brother in that prairie landscape for the holidays. Time spent cooking and visiting together in the area that used to be home. I almost didn't but I chose to go to the store. Levi was predictably in the back room, but he saw me. Rather, he said he heard the sound of my voice as I talked to a passerby. Levi and I chatted as easily as we always had, a romantic tension in the air between us. It felt so good it hurt. In the setting of the store, I knew he wouldn't bare his soul. Those words weren't meant for here. But his eyes said, *I can't be what you need me to be but oh how I want to. How I wish I could. But I can't. I know myself and I can't.* That's what his eyes said as I shared my troubles in letting him go and missing him so. Somewhere inside, it dawned on me that I'd seen these eyes before.

I could see him melt inside with comfort and joy as he took in the love in my eyes. But only for a moment before his trepidation, hiding, and deep fear took hold once again. Oh how those waves in him were so achingly familiar too.

Tentatively, I ventured, "Life up north is feeling settled. The thing that lingers is you. There's not a day I don't think of you."

"Really? Wow. Thanks, I think of you. A few days a week." His shoulders sighed in relief.

"I know it's improbable that we could be together." I was really asking one last time, but I couldn't ask it out of love. I didn't want him to live with the guilt of what I knew was the answer he'd come to. I guess I just needed to hear it clearly. Or else I hoped to hear that the lie I knew better than to tell myself was true, that his love for me had sparked a fire to surpass his limitations and reach for the stars together.

What he said next hurt. It was bluntly honest because, as always, he heard my heart's speak. "Yeah, I guess I'll keep doing me, my routine, it works. Things are better now than they used to be." His nervous manners were back. They had been from the moment I saw him. But he still stood tall, just as I taught him to in his kitchen. He couldn't look at me as he said those words, only to the ground and his vegetables. I couldn't look at him either. It was the truth I'd known, but I had to take a moment to receive it.

I looked up at him. "I appreciate you and every moment we have had together. I've thought about us. I understand that you have a fear of change inside you that made it hard for you to adjust to me, to how I felt, to having me in your life. And when I felt you resist, it sparked my own fear, or pains really. It made me take a big step back because I felt unwanted. We did that again and again, wanting each other but not realizing we were triggering each other's fears. But none of those fears were us. They weren't between us. They were within us from pasts or experiences we don't need anymore. What remained through all the time that we spent together and apart was the care we had for each other. It's why we held on and drew back to one another. Our love." He listened intently, leaning in, nodding.

"Yeah, that makes a lot of sense. I never thought of it that way."

"If we were ever to be together, I'd want to know. Because I'm no longer living inside waiting for you, waiting for someday."

"I understand. Maybe I'll get my truck up and running for the highway. Maybe I'll look up the route. I'm sure there's jobs up there. It sounds real nice."

"It sounds wonderful. But when I leave here, I won't hear from you. You'll go home at the end of your workday, and you'll work out to push me out of your mind. And then you'll be okay without me. Okay enough that you'll keep on living life as it is. Is that right? Because that's how it has been. And I understand that because I know it hurts when we part. I know it hurts to face that pain. But . . ." I didn't have the heart to finish the thought in words.

"It is. It's hard. Because you're there and I'm here. I know you were it for me. You're the one. It's just hard for me. It's hard for me to do it, you know?" *This was always going to be him. It would always have been us. Even though I loved him, it would have been my life, even after we'd come this far.* In a large sense, people are who they are until *they* grow.

"I know." I replied. "You're a beautiful person Levi. You and the times we've shared will always be special to me." He glowed. But I knew that glow would only last until I was gone. I could not sustain him. It was a hard pill to swallow in that groundbreaking moment. But a truth I accepted with grace as I let him go. It was what he wanted, and it was what I needed to do for myself. To hold on any longer would only bring pain to us both. It was time. I said the words I knew I must.

"I realize I have to let you go Levi. I want you to remember that I love you. Always." I touched his arm. I'm not sure if I wanted him to hear, "I'm going to let you go now. I need you to know that." or if I had to hear myself say those words, maybe both. I had my answer now. I'd needed to say it. Closure brings peace to the heart and the mind, it rests the soul. But the words I needed most were telling him, "I love you, always."

When he echoed my words, his heart filled his voice, but it didn't reach past the wall I now held between us.

In that moment, I mustered the dignity I had and walked without looking back until I got to the door. At the door, I had to look back at him. It meant something. He knew it did. I did too. I looked back at the last moment as I turned to leave the store, and with a small wave I was gone. In that moment, he was a reminiscent image. He stood behind the display, watching me. He likened a hiding man standing behind the low rack of new inventory surrounded by his old familiar walls, his shelter in a world that never changed. Safe yet afraid.

Our lives are made up of many choices, large and small, and those choices define the pathways of our lives. With those moments shared in our last time, Levi made a choice that freed us both. I made a choice that freed myself. Levi's love was unending, real, and pure. But it had its limits. That's what makes us human. By Levi's choice, and by my dawning truths, as weeks and months passed by, I found the painful strength to let him go. I heard many other things also inside of me as I let him go. Like this:

Real love exists in this world. Many of us have it. I'd felt its gifts with him. But just because it was real didn't mean it was right. A critical crossroads that's key to our happiness is deciding what love *and* life is right for us. I suppose we both made the choice in our own way that day and every other day we'd said goodbye.

Love isn't perfect because people aren't perfect, nor are we meant to be. I got to feel the powerful flow of loving my partner's imperfections as a perfect fit. I got to feel the energy flowing through me of unconditional romantic love.

Reflection: The Sunsets' Painter

Blue brush strokes curl across the evening sky amidst a radiant yellow. These colors calmed and breathed the peace of night into the vibrancy of the setting sun. Like God had freshly placed them there for those who look up. A symbol of the endings that beget beginnings in our lives, sunsets and sunrises are equally colorful for a reason. For they are equally insightful times rich in the hues of new insights and growth inside and out of ourselves.

Life: Processing

Looking back, I realize too that maybe he was the strong one. That he knew he couldn't be the man I needed; that our dream together wouldn't work in practice. I suppose that could be true. That what we were to each other was just right; was beautiful. I held faith that I was on my path to a choice to draw closer. A well deeper. A hold tighter. A gaze matched, for the eyes are the windows to the soul.

The love I'd find would still make me come alive. It'd still electrify my skin and everything within. It would be a home for my thoughts and passions to free my mind when I'm with him and enchant my spirit when we're apart. But it would be more than that. It would be stable, steady, in a way that eased everything too. And he would love me without reserve. Want me without restraint. Maybe my love would find me. Maybe *life* had to find me first.

There's another different feeling that comes with this letting go. It's the realization that this is the start of a blank page, a chapter yet unwritten. It's a feeling of excitement I haven't felt before. I know good things are coming for me. God has them in store. They started today with the sprouting of a crocus in the morning sun in the dawning of a brand-new day.

Change is a prerequisite to following your dreams. It requires sacrifice. Courage. Bold moves. Most of all tenacity. I wasn't in that moment quite yet, but with time, I was able to finally set him free from my heart. And in letting him go, I discovered that letting go allows for letting in. I let my plan go to let God's plan in. I let go of my old ways of being in the world to let new concepts of what I believe come through, so strongly that I couldn't operate the way I did before. With the acceptance of every new truth, I felt closer to who I truly was, and I came to realize that letting go wasn't just a painful thing. It made room. It made room for a person to grow. Within me and within my life. I could grow in new ways that breathed life into the soul, the mind, the heart, life itself. And for that, I could find love again. A love God made for me.

Reflection: Leaves

What if a tree held onto old growth? It was once new and remarkable, especially as it unfolded in spring. But just on the dawn of autumn's letting go, when the tree prepares its goodbye to this season of life, that's when it looks most beautiful of all.

Such a vulnerability it takes for that tree to stand bare from November through May. A lonely, barren, cold winter it stands through as a true sign of faith.

I remember as a child thinking winter trees look dead. Maybe in those barren times, parts of ourselves die with those magnificent leaves. But winter is bound to bring new again. Water it, tend to it, your tree, and life will grow again.

Letting go seemed to have come in as many forms as there were colors of leaves on the iridescent trees. Grandma, friends, childhood home, the life I'd built all my life, places and people always known, my mother's happiness, moments gone by, so many little things. Every time my grandma said, "Grandma loves you." in her kitchen by the carport door. Every crevice of their well-lived home of six decades or more. My friends and the adventures we lived in our own innocent ways. The people that seemed like family found in the most unexpected places, as they so often are. My childhood home, the frame for our memories. The places no one knew meant something to me, but I did. The spirit of every child whom I got to love. Routines and spontaneity that, come to think of it, comforted much. The bashful look and tenderness of one life-touching friend.

Sometimes, I live there in reverie. It leaves me knowing what that tree would feel if it didn't cast its colorful beauty in the fall. Dead things a branch holds onto poison it within, rob its nutrients, its joy, until there's nothing left. Thank God He prunes our tree. For if not, we'd surely know by now the sorrow of yesterday's tomorrow.

The cycles of nature are something to be thankful for. Their role in our life's process allows us to renew in the same, inspiring way.

Reflection: Reflections Beyond

I learned one more thing. When you invite God into the hurdles you're facing, self-efficacy can expand. God didn't make us for a challenge we couldn't surpass with the support of His light.

We each have within us the necessary forces to meet every challenge we face. Overcoming; surpassing, requires you to face your inner joys, wounds, truths, the dimensions of yourself, all the while with your hand in His. Only with the courage to face yourself within and without can you truly surpass, deepen, and thrive. You will.

When I invited God into the hurdles I was facing, he Gracefully took my hand. In His Power, He walked with me when I felt alone. He picked me up when I felt I couldn't. He knelt with me when kneeling was all I could do. Because transmuting pain takes faith, hope, strength, and the persistence of love.

Just as He tends to the needs of the milkweed plant in its seeds in the pod, God has a way of laying forth the plans to our heart's dreams before we even realize they are there. When we place our hope in faith, when we invite Him into the places where our heart aches and needs, letting go and letting God is just as beautiful as the wisp of that milkweed seed as its star shape releases into the wind.

Life: Dear Levi,

You were my first true love. A light ignited in my heart and my spirit the moment you entered my life. I can still remember the day. Your nerves put me at ease just as I put your nerves to ease. Two souls who saw each other for who they are on the golden inside, wholesome and pure, burning and enduring. An instant connection that electrified the spirit and awakened the heart. We were fit and fashioned for each other, perfectly, if only for a time. And for all the heartbreak that comes with letting you go, no pain of loss could ever dim the blessing of every touch of your fingers on my skin, the moment of true open happiness on your face I knew I'd put there, the hold of your hand, the saunter of your walk, your slow and handsome voice, your bashful blush, humor and play, your powerful character all the more. The love you expressed to me was the most earnest I've ever known.

My heart breaks as I write this, but it is matched in gratitude. I want you to know that you healed my heart. You made my heart and soul feel seen in a true way. You listened to me with everything in you. You reveled in my voice. You revered me for *who I am.* You loved my soul.

You told me once that I brought you back to the living, and so many other beautiful things that allowed me to know my heart had touched yours. Healed you too. Transformed. Here's what you did for me. You made it safe to love again. You gave my heart faith it may have lost without you in it. You taught me tough lessons of true grit through loving you, but all the while you made me feel cherished, adored, respected, admired, understood, revered, felt, seen, and heard, most of all forever. You showed me true love never ends. I know within you there are binds that do not allow us to hold one another, to grasp the magic and partake in our dreams we had together. For four years, I held onto that magic, to you inside my heart, but "someday" didn't come. I understand that too. Because I know you. But I have to live again. With my whole heart. I don't think

I realized how much of it you had till life called me to look. I Loved you. I loved all of you with all my might within. Every dimension of your spirit was gold to me. Deep inside of me you have lived. But now, that is where your memory will live. Not a place to dwell, but as a golden thread in the tapestry that is my life. Sewn in love, the thread keeps on weaving. I take my heart back as my own. It is my piece of gold to hold onto. To cherish and desire for it beats every day within for me. And strengthened by the power of all that has been, anything can be for me.

I release you. I pray that God take care of you, heart, mind, body, and soul, knowing He will. I pray He do the same for me, knowing He will. And I pray that God will heal each of us, fill my heart with all the light and love it can hold, feeling deserving and accepting all the while and loving the same in return. Isn't that true love? Dare I say isn't that the deeper part that kept us perpetually apart? Lastly, I thank God for you, for healing, real love, for lasting lessons learned, for pure magic, for us.

My whole heart wants you, but it deserves to be wanted too. I want to give all of my love and receive all of yours, but I know that this is something we are not capable of. We never were. That is the wall we met time and time again and yet I was not ready to face. Rather I turned away from that wall only to return to the same room and space again and again. Because we felt good. That's love. But I deserve love as immense as I am willing to give. I deserve love that waits. I deserve love that receives readily, with a thirst that has been waiting a lifetime for me and sees my soul and cannot live without me but only by me. A love that shines bright from within each alone but poureth over together. Love that prevails by the earnest will of each other. A will possessed by both equally, forcefully, by sheer act of loving. No holds back.

From this day forward, I will not hold myself back beyond these rights. I walk straight forward into my destiny led by my heart and soul within because these things are what I emit to the world and what the world sees in me as I glow in it. I am.

I live my life now empowered for my journey ahead, knowing God is with me, and so am I.

Thank you. I love you. Goodbye.

Allie

I tucked the letter in a shoe box where I kept mementos of good memories. That's where Levi would live.

Reflection: Universal Words

Different cultures are worth learning. The more you learn, the more you realize that we're all connected to common heart strings. It's why words that don't exist in my language still resonate with my heart.

Like *jung* from Korea. *Jung* means the connection between two people that cannot be severed. This word makes me think of history. Of people who are gone from one another's lives yet etched in each other's hearts, minds, stories. It's an unspoken power, this kind of bond that too often seems mutilated by differences and distance. What matters to the heart is love, and anywhere you've invested your heart, you've invested love. No matter what happens, love lives always. *Jung.*

Jung reminds me of my father. It reminds me of Levi. It reminds of the friends I love dearly no matter the miles that part us. Choices define our lives. Most definitive are the choices we make with our hearts. All of the best, and all of the toughest, choices are those I've made with my heart. Perhaps that's what brings me back to *jung.* With this truthful word, we are given a freedom of knowing that no matter where our heart leads us, love gives us a home, love is never lost, love lives always. It lives in the eyes of a friend. It lives in the heart of a lover. It lives in the memory of a day gone by, looked back on, but let go. That's *jung.*

Jung is a word for the past.

There's a word in Spanish, *linda. Linda* is a word for the present; the future.

It's unlike any word we have in English because it can mean something is beautiful both to the eyes and to the heart. When I see the way that Marshall and Annie look at one another, *linda* often comes to mind.

Linda is what I feel when I watch Bentley's shoulder-shaking laugh. *Linda* is the late summer sunset over the inland north woods lake, just me and the water and the woods and a warm breeze. *Linda* is when Winston and Amelia fuss at each other but really at the root it's care, knowing each other 74 years well. It's the smell mixed with the effervescence of the green when I gaze upon the birch and the pine. It's the amble of the land and its homesteaders when taking a drive. *Linda*, when I reflect on these things, all comes down to that glowing light of love we feel when something is special to us; truly marvelous. And I want to have as much *linda* in my life as I can take in. With attention. With appreciation. With purpose. With ambition towards it.

Simultaneously, we must be accepting *jung* whilst embracing *linda* to truly continue flowing in life. It keeps our hearts open, our passions burning, our dreams expansive no matter how they morph and re-sculpt us.

Reflection: Synergy

There's a concept of energy wherein two wholes come together to create one. Imagine. Two equal, complete energies, whole as they stand, coming together in unison to create something entirely new. It seems impossible that all that wholeness could fit together into one thing. But that's a magic principle of energy. It's one of the most beautiful principles if you ask me. It's what I strive for. Because when two wholes come together, anything is possible, every power, every dream, comes together into one storehouse that can move their world into a new vision. In a way not yet envisioned before. The cup poureth over. Yes, two parts make a whole, but two wholes, that's the magic of synergy. This is the kind of love I would have someday.

Reflection: Inherent

I came upon a baby deer curled up in the grass. She still looked wet, and her eyes still had that hazy blue. She wasn't startled at all by my presence. I kept a respectful distance from her as I watched in awe. She lifted her little head and smelled the air around her, touching the grass with her nose. Her lip lifted with each sniff. The sun was bright and warm. Then, she decided to stand. She put her legs underneath her and took her first steady steps, her legs almost unnoticeably quivering as the thin fawn made her way toward the safe forest. What a gift to watch her very first steps! She was sure. She knew her way. She was following her instincts.

Reflection: Dandelions

The sunshine felt good on the bare skin of my shoulders as I flopped the kneeling pad and spade down in the sandy soil of our yard. That quick draining, fine sand, was not too poor in nutrients to scare off the weeds. Those grew in multitude by the year. As I plopped the bag of fresh crocus bulbs I'd purchased onto our lawn, a bright idea put a glint in my eye. For each of these thirty little bulbs I planted, I'd stick them in a spot where a dandelion once was. What a nice way to plant. One less weed, one more flower. That way, if they never come up, at least I still beautified our yard. I shimmied at the genius moment, excited for a good hard job ahead.

The spade was just the tool for the job, but those weeds were aplenty. I didn't have to look hard to choose where to dig. I decided to pick the ugliest monsters to tackle. They were like goliaths.

I had a strategy for attack. Digging my spade straight down into the dirt, I made a circumference around the plant, taking as little ground with each one as possible. I went as deep as the blade would go, trying to get all the tap root. Those big guys tugged out with ease. Every once in a while, I plucked a small one. But then there were a few, some that looked rather normal and I expected to be reasonably simple. But they ended up being the hardest to tackle of all! I'd follow my routine only to find that their taproot forked out in different directions and wanted to break off at the end. I had to dig deeper, wider, gentler to master the art of cleanly breaking them free. If not, I'd be leaving a piece behind to start the weed all over again.

As I encountered this pattern again and again, I began to feel a connection. Digging up these dandelions was a lot like digging into ourselves to extract the weeds that took root in our hearts. Some require simple identification, acknowledgement, and removal. Others, unexpectedly or not, need extra care, gentleness, close attention, more time, to completely remove. Most importantly, a hole cannot be left in their wake. It is necessary to plant new and beautiful things where holes are created in our hearts. That's how we tend to our heart's gardens.

It's okay to leave some weeds. No garden is perfect. Though weeds are seen as a nuisance that choke out what we want in our soil, environments need plants with taproots, like the dandelion. They serve a purpose to stir things up in soil that has long stood still and stagnant. They unsettle and oxygenate the soil so that new things can grow from deep within sleeping parts of the Earth.

After a dandelion has been rooted for some time, it goes through its own metamorphosis of sorts. Its flower closes up into a dried spiral having finished taking in the sun in its display. But something is going on beneath the dried surface of its crumpled leaves and petals that appear to be done. Seeds are preparing to unfold in the release of a perfect sphere. As if they'd been there all along waiting to be upheld, because they have been. Waiting for the young child who didn't pick the dandy flower to pull this white and whimsical counterpart and cast their wishes upon the blue sky ahead. With unabashed trust that wish may come with the ability to let that wish go where it may. The innocence to live in the very moment that lies before.

Some dandelions are meant for moments like these. Times when the weeds of scars plant roots of heartache, leaving us feeling crumpled, when hope is dry only to remember that childhood innocence of wishes and trust and faith. When we make a wish in faith, we can let go of its outcome and let the planting of the seed carry it wherever the wind takes that wish, thus taking us. Somehow, that's always far better than where our own begging thoughts lead. It's raw, authentic, purifying, deepening, transformative.

I know that there are many summers to life, just as there are many autumns, winters, and springs. Each one serves its unique purpose. Each one carries with it the promise of wings like these freedoms that carry us.

Some of our gardens' weeds give us the opportunity to share our strength and learning with others who walk a similar road. These transmuting seeds are meant to be cast, to be planted in their hearts in healing and understanding. Touching someone in this way touches us right back. It's a healing that's delivered and received through the deep spiritual gift of heart-learned giving. One that keeps casting another seed gracefully out a little farther into the swirling winds.

Children are often some of the people with the purest hearts, untouched yet by the world. They see the beauty in a dandelion. I can't count the times I've been given one as a gift from the schoolyard. Laid upon my desk as a token of love and appreciation.

I think weeds are often a matter of perspective. Some are necessarily a nuisance. Some things need to be weeded for the purpose that they get in the way of living our best life. Only we know which weeds we have and why. Only we know what to do with them to achieve our highest journeys. That's a task done between us and God. So with the discernment of a gardener, we step foot into our hearts with Him, spade in hand, extract them with tenderness handled with consideration and care, examine our sorrows, feel the contours of their pain where they've grown into our hearts, and treat them with tenderness, for that's the way we truly take their burrowing harm away. When we're through, we feel empowered, for we did it for ourselves, within ourselves, with God by our side, hand in hand. We take in the view of the dandelions left in our earth and know that they are purposeful to our life. We know that some of the most beautiful moments in our lives lie ahead in the opportunities to help someone else see their own dandelion flower, show them how they're growing, what their conquering, the beauty in their reflection of the sun if only they see their light, their hope, and their dreams. Just like those seeds.

The yellow blossoms radiate sunlight back up to the sky as if to ask, "What defines a flower and a weed?" Are they always so clearly different? Weeds too, are God's creation. All serve a role. Just as these fine plants have served a role in my life. Both the flowers and the weeds that rooted in my spirit have helped the garden of my heart grow and flourish into who I am now.

In the soil of my heart, I've uprooted some dandelions and kept others in my soil. Dandelion taproots splayed the different kinds of pains driven in. The sculpting those pains did to my character, my thought processes, and my heart, are what made me come to understand life as I do. Their complexities taught me how to hold trials and how to hold myself. They oxygenated the soil of my heart because I've learned a deeper compassion, greater balance, truer acceptance, forgiveness, boundaries, discernment, and self-love. Discernment to know which lessons were valuable and what to uproot and plant anew. Like weeds, our gifts in life are seen through how we look at them and our garden is tending by how we look into ourselves.

Life: Lovefilling

It inspires me that my great grandmother is buried here in these north woods. That our family laid roots here in this northern land makes me wonder at how our ancestors lay the groundwork to our futures; how we lay the groundwork for our children; how every interconnected life forms a spiritual family tree not bound by blood but by love and a common path. It's inspiring how far the reaches of love can grow when they're interconnected.

From the time that I've walked this earth, I've come to believe in a fact. It's that within every human being lies a void we are endowed with the spiritual responsibility to fill. A void is a delicate thing that needs to be handled as such. In a void lies a depth unknown in spaces found only by the soul itself.

It's in our hands how we choose to treat our void. Do we feel it? Do we find it? Do we start the search? Do we end it? Do we muster the courage to flow where it leads us? For filling the void ourselves takes the tenacity of walking through the darkness while holding a light. Can you see where your void is filled? Or do you only see absence? Do you know the presence of God? Do you ask for it? Take God's hand in yours; step into the void. Step into the journey of luminescence and watch it unfurl around you and in you.

I had to recognize the fact the only void I could heal was my own. I couldn't fill my fathers or Levi's, nor can I fill any other person that I wanted to fix. Love can heal. Love can make miracles. Love can conquer all, but only the healing of self-love can mend the tears that form in our spirit. Voids must be filled with the gathering of light. It's the kind we harness within from the things that spark our passion, fuel our spirit, bring us epiphanies of joy, resolutions of peace, moments of love that percolate into a new way of being. The harvesting and cultivation of light into darkened voids is an art worth taking up. In its process lies a masterpiece. In its completion lies a fulfillment beyond realization.

Life: What We Choose to do with Pain

A dear friend of mine, Winston, lost his mother when he was only four years old. Winston was raised by his sisters and a father at a loss. The void his mother's absence left rested in him for all his 97 years. An acute awareness that brought him not only pain but appreciation of all mothers around the world. So with pain came a special kind of love for his wife, Amelia, and a special way of caring for every mother who stepped across his awareness. Doesn't that harvest light for the world? I believe every pain has an opportunity to bring a compounded beauty to the world when it's channeled through love, into love.

I felt compelled to fix my father because I felt that was the way to reach his soul, to help him and us, and in moments I felt like I could. Just as I reached into students, friends, even strangers in need, to heal them, and oftentimes I did, we did, together. Those breakthroughs are the quiet triumphs of my life. They create an uncanny bond between souls that at once cannot perish or be outwardly understood.

I choose to believe that, in moments, I did feel my father's soul beneath the layers of his many skins, and that, to me, is beautiful. But that's what they were, moments in a lifetime. A lifetime can't be spent for moments, waiting amongst the many questions that swirl in the midst. Just as waiting for love, living a lifetime for moments wasn't enough for me anymore. Life is meant to be *lived* an entire life; it deserves to be filled. Therein lies the choice: to live to fill thy void or to live to fill thy life. Standing at the crossroads, fully aware, I took the courageous step into the great unknown. I took God's hand and a deep breath. I let out and let in. I fueled my peak; I filled my life. I lived.

Reflection: The Excitement of Faith

Last fall, I purchased crocus bulbs at the store. People reasoned with me that their chances of rising up out of this earth come spring were questionable if not slim in the extreme northern drifts. But I always held a fondness for them. There was a yard I passed by on Elm Street where they grew every year, the first blossoms of a new season, and they always brought a smile to my heart. So I bought them. I invested in the hope that they would rise even after the weighted drifts of winter's snow and the cold had seeped into the space all around them. Because that's what they were made to do. They were made to be the first to sprout, sometimes right through those last slushy piles of snow.

God makes us that way too. He makes us to weather the conditions we encounter. And He gives us the power to sprout back up after each cold winter's season with just that same kind of hope and faith in Love, in Him. Aren't they one in the same?

After the private winter my heart went through, in that wavering, when we moved up north, I felt a wavering faith at times that my heart could bloom. But I'd forgotten. God made me for such a time as this. He made me to not just endure this, but to make beauty out of this. Because I am His. He lives inside me, like the peace and joy and strength and openness in my heart that is an ever part of my spirit. Whenever I go out in nature, I am reminded of this noble truth.

Last fall, when I planted each new crocus bulb, I planted them in place of dandelions. I fussed over their winter ahead. I knew mine would be cold too. Little did I know, a few would be lost to hungry squirrels in a matter of a week, a hungry deer. It was a risk of growing I shrugged, undiscouraged. But after those cold months, a time mostly hunkered inside and alone, and sometimes testing resources, those flowers remembered what they were made for and awakened their power inside. With magnificent color in the golden light of the sun, they sprung forth from the sandy soil. They bloomed.

Life: **Fueling**

Sometimes, the truths in our stories that we feel but don't face are the ones that hurt us the most. When I grew up and faced my truth, I realized that even with all the beautiful, abundant, unconditional love I received from my mom, feeling that worthlessness from dad over and over as I was growing up became a part of the way I felt about myself. I thought that it was me. I thought I wasn't enough. I somehow wasn't worth loving in his eyes, even if I was adored in my mom's. His actions and his words told me he didn't want me. It wasn't until I understood that it wasn't me, let go of trying to change his heart, and accepted what he could give that I finally found peace. Because a person has to want to change, want to love, and he didn't want mine. I couldn't teach or love him into living any differently because the choice of change lay in his hands, never in mine.

It took me years to overcome my illusion that I could change our world. Years to learn that love nor support nor guidance could build a heart up from its dwelling place without its own will. But I had to try. For as much as trying gave me pain, it gave me peace. For "What if?" is a ravenous question love won't allow.

We all have challenges in our lives. How we face them is what defines us. The choices we make in facing them are the choices that shape our futures, that shape our character, who we become. In small ways, we make those choices every day. In large ways, I believe the choices we make come down to our dreams. Dreams are what fuels us to surpass life's challenges and make our world better not just for us but for all. God plants within us dreams. Within us lies the choice to be true to those dreams, to be true to ourselves. When we say yes to our dreams, God lays out the plan with us and sets our path. As we rise to choose our dreams every day, He meets us, step for step.

As a teacher, I have seen so many of my students, whom, in my heart, are truly young friends, walk a path of pain wishing if only I could take it away. And I want you to know something. Most often, people, whether they are kids or adults, do the best they can with what they have. Your loved ones were once children too. They have their own strengths and hurt places from another time well before you even came.

If you have a challenge like mine, it isn't you. You are more than enough. You are beautiful. I want you to know this too: I know as a kid you don't have a lot of control over your circumstances, but make the best of what you have. Be good to you and to those who love you. Show compassion for others because you are good. And above all else know this:

There are times in our lives that shape and mold us. They try us. They bring us closer to who we want to be because the choices we make in the valleys define the refined form we embody at the peaks. Draw close to your spirit, to God, and you'll come to feel these challenging seasons as growing pains of the soul and I truly mean it when I say, the valleys fuel the peaks. I know because my own have time and time again.

The valleys sowed the fabric of my faith, and God stood by me every moment, even when I couldn't hear Him. The peaks gave me a love that I didn't hold for myself. Strength isn't just tested to the limits, it's stretched and pushed beyond that to achieve a greater new standard and lift up your life because, like any good Father, God wants best for His children. So you see, both those valleys and peaks are equal gifts.

I realized that I was a stronger person for having loved my dad and a lucky person for having had my mom. Who do you have in your life that you're lucky for? I accepted that my dad wasn't able to love me the way most do. By that acceptance, I finally started to let go of feeling not enough. The truth was that my dad was a hurting person inside, in a winding way that I could never fully understand. In a way, neither did he. We're all children inside in ways. We all have pieces of us that are fragile. Each does their best with what they have. And when people don't make the right choices for us, we must make them for ourselves. What I could give my dad was understanding in the form of forgiveness and compassion. Because he's my dad. And space because I'm worth it. And the reminder that no matter how old you are, I believe you are wise enough to see the truth. The truth is powerful enough to move mountains. Inside you and around you. The truth most of all, can set you free. It sets us free when we have courage to not only face our truth but do something about it.

And when we invite God into the pieces of our hearts that hurt, the places where we must face our truths, His hand holds ours. He walks us through step by step if only we trust in Him, if only we *see* Him the way He sees us. The way a soulmate sees another.

As I walked my journey to healing my heart with God, He took me far deeper than I ever knew I must go. Deeper than I ever looked before. And by taking those footsteps, the steps He cast the light on one by one, faithfully, I discovered a magic in my heart and dimensions of my soul I never realized. Through all the pain and anguish, there was a sense of renewal. And when I look back on it all, I see that for taking that deeper walk with God, I deepened into my soul. That deepening reflects through the eyes with which I see each day. I pour it out onto others like a gift to me that gives to the world. Because that's how God gives.

I soak in someone's words, breathe through hearts' aches, see past eyes and into a soul's needs, I speak with God because God speaks with me. It's what we're meant to do here because we are His children. I trust and listen to my heart again because I know my heart is where We meet. These are God's greatest gifts to me that ever give in reciprocity.

Reflection: God Lives in the Woods

I kneeled down by the stream. The running waters made my emotions feel like they could run out of me too. Or perhaps it was the intimacy of being alone with nature that so ensafened me. The running of the water did not make my tears run, not this time. But it allowed me to release, quietly. It helped me feel myself and feel felt in return, by the woods. Like the woods knew my upheaval, my story, my resolve, and my return. They knew all that I'd walked through and the power I carried within, the abiding strength of love.

To let my sorrow run was no longer what I came here for. The reason I came was to be understood. To be enlivened. To wonder. And for the first time, in my heart, I felt safe in knowing that the learned path of the past was finally over. No longer did I have to brace myself for pain's revival. The memories could fade. Tension could trickle out like this water that flowed to the sea. That's not to say that the past didn't matter. For it happened. Both beautiful and hard, every bit of it built me. God walked with me. He helped me. And for that, my very nature was given more dimension. For all the things He showed me, He taught me, He handed me in Love and grace because . . .

God helped me know that mercy breeds new life.

He helped me understand that the lifetime of a soul paints a person.

He held my hand when I felt alone.

He helped me see that compassion goes far beyond and far deeper than human need to an earnest desire to understand. It comes without even needing to know all that makes a man, but instead simply giving grace. That when you open yourself fully to compassion, you move beyond compassion to the true essence of forgiveness.

He planted seeds, pruned my tree, and led me here.

He protected me with dreams when someone's hatred for me became my own for myself.

He heard my thoughts that no one else did, felt my heart in wounded places left unshared, healed it with me so I could understand.

He gave birth to inspiration in my thoughts and answered my prayers, just as he does for you. He helped me see that patience softens the screaming soul.

He gave me the gift of my beautiful mother.

He helped me see that when you ask Him with a pure and open heart to lend His hand, He reaches out with the rainbow, every color, shade, and hue of Love. To journey with Him is to truly, deeply know Him. To walk a journey of *life*.

The more you know Him, the more you grow in Love because He is Love.

And the more you understand His Love for you, the more you see yourself the way God sees you.

He painted the sunsets and the northern skies.

He placed countless gifts of His people along my path to guide my way and my heart.

Love brought my father and me out of odds. Love brought me down roads of despair and closer to home than I've ever been. Love compelled me to dive into depths of my heart that ne'er would have been found were it not for the trials I chose to face head on. When we choose to face ourselves with God, He leads us through, and through His truths, He shows us dimensions of our heart waiting to be shared with the world.

Reflection: In the Woods' Eyes

Allie fell in love with the beauty in every person because she saw beauty in each person she met. It was by a temperament of the love she learned from that she searched for the best of love she could find for her. One that held the stars in his eyes and the moon in hers.

On Allie's trialed path to this pure, natural place of magic and truth, the land of the woods and the pond became what was, in fact, her path to Truth, Faith, and Love. Most of all, it was a journey home. But to a home that was more than a place. It was a home like she'd never seen, like coming home to herself. Homemade Allie come alive from the inside out. Because home was within her. It was on the path to home where she came to understand what it meant to be free.

Afterward

I used to teach students around the age of nine. I am convinced there's something about that age. Somewhere between the years of nine and eleven, a person is old enough to understand the world around them but not be jaded by it, to see the world with crystal clear eyes of truth, to be close to themselves at the core of who they truly are. I think this age is the most open of years, the time when a child can make the greatest impact on their own lives by the path they choose to follow. I believe this because of what I saw in the eyes and voices of the beautiful young people I was privileged to teach and know. Most of all, I knew it by the way they connected with the world and with me, the way they responded to the impact I tried to make in their lives. They taught me that within every person lies a desire to do good if only someone lovingly chooses to believe it, and by believing it, expect it. I witnessed that, no matter the capacity of our hearts, we can only receive as much love from the outside world as we receive from our own inside world. That a child can beautifully rise above mountainous trials when they have the will to. That the persistent will to be happy is a true sign of strength. That children need to talk about life and choices and feelings in grown-up ways; it empowers them to make choices that remain true to their best selves. That children are, at the core, equals to adults; souls with the same ability to see and feel and understand, and even give back.

Over my years of teaching, I shared many adventurous stories with my students. I told them about people in ways that had spoken morals and truths to my heart because I knew it would serve theirs too. Because of my deep love for each child in my little family of a classroom, it was so important to me to impart every bit of wisdom I could to empower them for their journey called life. You never know what heart might be listening to a story that inspires them to rise above to reach *their* highest peak. Through my stories, I shared my hard-carned wisdom clothed in humor. But I think I enjoyed telling stories as much as they liked listening for sharing in their joy.

Through my stories, I taught them survival tips because when you love a kid like a mother, you can't help but want them to be safe. True life stories with tidbits of science and survival tips I wanted them to remember. Important facts like: Know that when the water on a Great Lake has no waves, the current will pull you out. Waves tell you that the water is coming into shore, but without them, it goes out. Be ever aware of your place and surroundings in water. My classes heard this message loud and clear, but most of all, they loved my animated telling of the tale through the years. Animated because storytelling was my passion, and passions shared are an infectious energy. They laughed till they cried. For them, I under-emphasized the circumstances and overemphasized the humor of my thoughts and the lessons to be learned.

I liked the way my students would wiggle in their seats and exchange knowing grins when they knew one was about to begin. I also liked how even though I let them think we're totally off topic from the lesson, which is really sort of fun, I'd have an even bigger lesson waiting to be identified inside that story. One about life.

I didn't realize that my love for those children was preparing me to write. Rehearsing me to tell my tale. God has a way of working through love.

Storytelling, lesson sharing, thought provoking, soul-stirring, are all acts of love for me. They come from my heart, and my heart goes out to yours. Directly, with love. Because I sincerely wish that you may experience something better for having heard or pondered it. Simply, that's what storytelling is to me. And as my reader, a person who has taken such great time to invest in my story, I appreciate your heart and what you have to offer this world. Please go out and honor it. Love yourself, your kin, and your life with your whole heart. Live from the soul.

About the Author

Dear Reader,

Thank you for taking the time to consider my words. I hope they evoke a deeper connection to your own heart as you traverse your life's journey. Living with the gift and responsibility of being an Empath, I have always sensed and cared for people acutely. Applying this innate connection with people and nature, it was important to me to serve others. Writing has been a gift to me, for it's the way my heart breathes all that it feels. I'm thankful to be able to share this gift with each of you. I sincerely hope it serves the evolution of your soul as it has my own.

Alongside writing, I love to live an active lifestyle that includes running, biking, hiking trails, nature, and people. I reside among the rolling hills and savanna oaks of Wisconsin's Driftless region, where from I conduct virtual and in-person events. Each of you matter so much; I'd love to hear from you and be in touch. If you'd wish to be connected, please reach out to me at shelbykottemann@gmail.com.

Warmly,

Shelby

Reviews

"This powerful author picture-painted her heart and soul through deep, unique expressions of words and experiences. Her technique and style of writing keeps one wondering what happens next. Allie's story is of a young lady who finds herself, her value and worth through emotional and mental abuse of one parent, a genuine love from the other, and a romantic relationship that appeared right, yet was detrimental to herself. Allie learns growth and enhancement through forgiveness of herself and others. She uses the science of nature, a personal journey with God, and right choices to create a must read, life changing book. You will be left with inspirational thoughts, a positive mindset, and a desire to achieve your best."
—**Toni Stone Bruce**, CEO/Founder Precious Stones 4 Life LLC, Author, Life Coach, Health/Wellness Advocate

"*Evolution of a Soul* is a profound book to read and cherish. Shelby uses beautiful imagery from nature, as well as painful anecdotes from life, to show what it means to have and grow faith. Read it slowly because the truths take time to fully develop in your soul. Then cherish it, like a fond memory that is remembered over and over."
—**Elda Robinson**, Retired Teacher, Facebook: Bowtie Shoes

"The author Shelby Kottemann is amazing as she guides the reader into her heart along with her emotions. Her unity with nature touched me deeply as I felt the connection for myself. I enjoyed her relationships and how she brought the reader along on her personal journey of growth. Through her growing she has learned the importance of allowing things to take shape and fly. A must read."
—**Karen Wright**, International Best Selling Author, *Now or Never, Shine Baby Shine*
https://www.shinenowornever.com

"Graceful story of struggle, acceptance, patience, love, disappointments, wisdom, and the lessons that come along with it. Detailed parallels and observations with nature descriptions and animals invite you to be part of this story. Beautiful, heart-felt journey of challenging life moments turned into lessons. Great read!"
—**Elle Ballard**, Speaker, leadership Trainer, and Founder of Women of the World Network
www.elleballard.com

Made in the USA
Monee, IL
26 November 2021

0d1af953-5a89-40ca-a813-9ae6bdea8ccfR01